READING

- **Comprehension** - **Spelling** - **Grammar** - **Review**

3

Contents

Year Planner

	Week 1	Week 2	Week 3	Week 4	Week 5	Week 6	Week 7	Week 8	Week 9
Comprehension	Finding facts and information	Drawing conclusions	Point of view	Think marks	Making predictions	Finding facts and information	Compare and contrast	Cause and effect	Word study
Spelling	Short and long vowel sounds	shr and thr	Endings: et, it, ot	Digraphs: oy, oi	ch sound	Trigraphs: air, eer	Plurals: s, es	Silent b, l, h	Suffix: ing
Grammar	Common and proper nouns	Capitalization and proper nouns	Personal pronouns	Adjectives	Apostrophes for ownership	Action verbs	Capital letters in direct speech	Noun phrases	Linking verbs
Review	Spelling			Grammar			Comprehension		

	Week 10	Week 11	Week 12	Week 13	Week 14	Week 15	Week 16	Week 17	Week 18
Comprehension	Visualization	Main idea and details	Making inferences	Sequencing events	Compare and contrast	Point of view	Drawing conclusions	Main idea and details	Cause and effect
Spelling	Trigraph: igh	Suffix: ing	ei, ey, eigh	Endings: le, el, al	Suffix: ed	Homophones	Silent k, g, w	Suffixes: er, or	Digraphs: wh, ph, gh
Grammar	Simple past and present tense	Auxiliary verbs	Future tense	Progressive tense	Commas in lists	Plural nouns	Possessive pronouns	Writing addresses	Subject-verb agreement
Review	Spelling			Grammar			Comprehension		

	Week 19	Week 20	Week 21	Week 22	Week 23	Week 24	Week 25	Week 26	Week 27
Comprehension	Analyzing character actions	Finding facts and information	Point of view	Making connections	Finding facts and information	Making connections	Cause and effect	Visualization	Main idea and details
Spelling	Verb endings: ies, ied	augh and ough	Suffix: ed	Soft c and g sounds	Irregular past tense verbs	Endings: ery, ary, ory	Suffixes: ful, less	Silent letters t, n, u	Compound words
Grammar	End punctuation	Abstract nouns	Pronoun-antecedent agreement	Adverbs of time	Apostrophes for contractions	Prepositions	Adverbial phrases	Adjectival phrases	Ownership for plural nouns
Review	Spelling			Grammar			Comprehension		

	Week 28	Week 29	Week 30	Week 31	Week 32	Week 33	Week 34	Week 35	Week 36
Comprehension	Cause and effect	Making inferences	Making connections	Sequencing events	Visualization	Main idea and details	Sequencing events	Making inferences	Point of view
Spelling	squ, sch, sph	Suffix: y	Contractions	Irregular plurals	Suffix: ly	Trigraph: ear	Prefixes: un, dis, mis	Tricky words	Suffix: ness
Grammar	Comparative adjectives	Comparative adverbs	Quotation marks in direct speech	Saying, thinking, and feeling verbs	Punctuating sentences	Simple sentences	Conjunctions	Compound sentences	Complex sentences
Review	Spelling			Grammar			Comprehension		

Shugg's Pet Octopus

Finding facts and information
To find facts and information in a text, ask the questions **Who? What? Where?** or **When?** The answers can be clearly seen in the text.

Read the passage.

Highlight where Shugg and Katie were going.

Underline what Duke asked Shugg.

Later, as Shugg and Katie walked home through the park, Duke stepped out from behind a tree. "Trying to scare me, were you?"

"No," said Shugg.

Duke snatched Shugg's backpack and threw it up into a very tall tree. He stood under the tree with his hands on his hips. "Now let's see you climb up and get it."

Circle how Duke got Shugg's backpack.

Color where Duke threw Shugg's backpack.

Circle the correct answer for each question.

1 **Where** were Shugg and Katie going?
a to school   b to the park   c home   d to the beach

2 **What** does Duke ask Shugg?
a May I look inside your backpack?   b May I look at your octopus?
c Where can we play this afternoon?   d Were you trying to scare me?

3 **How** did Duke get Shugg's backpack?
a He snatched it.   b He asked for it.   c He bought it.   d He tossed it.

4 **Who** threw Shugg's backpack?
a Duke   b Miss Stinger   c Katie   d Cal

5 **Where** did Shugg's backpack land?
a up a tree   b under a tree   c in the lake   d under a chair

RL.3.1 Ask and answer questions to demonstrate understanding of a text, referring explicitly to the text as the basis for the answers.

Shugg's Pet Octopus

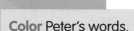
Read the whole story

Read the passage.

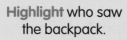
Highlight who saw the backpack.

Put a box around where the backpack was.

Circle when Shugg raided the pantry.

Peter looked down at the backpack poking out from under the bed. Then he shook his head. "Nah! Not even you would bring home an octopus."

Later that night, Shugg raided the pantry. He found a tin of crabmeat and some lobster-flavored noodles. He opened both and pushed them under the bed.

Color Peter's words.

Underline the things that Shugg found in the pantry.

1. **Who** looked down at the backpack?

   _____

2. **Where** was the backpack?

   _____

   _____

3. **What** did Peter say?

   _____

   _____

4. **When** did Shugg raid the pantry?

   _____

5. **What** did Shugg find in the pantry?

   _____

   _____

RL.3.1 Ask and answer questions to demonstrate understanding of a text, referring explicitly to the text as the basis for the answers.

3

Short and long vowel sounds

The vowels, **a, e, i, o, u**, can make a short or a long sound.

	Short	Long
a	hat	fame
e	bed	me
i	lid	blind
o	top	most
u	sun	cute

List   ① **Write the word.**

map   _____

name   _____

egg   _____

mine   _____

lid   _____

log   _____

cute   _____

sum   _____

mole   _____

mule   _____

glad   _____

slime   _____

frog   _____

black   _____

lump   _____

flame   _____

sink   _____

apple   _____

fled   _____

stole   _____

② **In a group.** Write the list word that belongs in each group.

a horse, donkey, _____

b atlas, chart, _____

c tap, plug, _____

d ran, escaped, _____

e wood, tree, _____

f bump, bulge, _____

g white, gray, _____

h goo, sludge, _____

i happy, pleased, _____

j pear, orange, _____

③ **Fill in the missing vowels.**

a n __ m __

b m __ l __

c l __ mp

d m __ n __

e st __ l __

f c __ t __

g m __ l __

h s __ m

④ **Name.**

a _____   **b** _____   **c** _____   **d** _____

L.3.2.F Use spelling patterns and generalizations in writing words.

Short and long vowel sounds

1 **Revise your spelling list from page 4.** Fill in the missing words.

a The _____ of Shelley's friend is Marko.

b I cracked the _____ into the mixing bowl.

c That's not your sweater, it's _____ .

d You should always put the _____ back on the jelly jar.

e Down by the water I could hear a _____ croak.

f The _____ of the fire was so hot it warmed the whole house.

g I was upset when someone _____ my bike.

h The _____ dug a deep tunnel underground.

i That puppy is very _____ .

Challenge words

2 **Write the word.**

spend _____

white _____

crest _____

tiger _____

smash _____

quake _____

hind _____

plume _____

extreme _____

behave _____

3 **Complete the sentence.**

a She counted six _____fluffy clouds.

b The _____stalked its prey through the jungle.

c Our house suffered damage during the _____.

d A parrot has a large yellow _____.

e Mom said if we didn't _____we wouldn't get dessert.

f The bird flew off, but left a white _____ behind.

g I didn't want to _____the rest of the day doing homework.

h The _____from the car accident outside woke me up.

4 **Another way to say it.** Which challenge word could replace the underlined word?

a He has a <u>feather</u> in his hat. _____

b The dog stood on its <u>back</u> legs. _____

c BMX is an <u>intense</u> sport. _____

d She is trying not to <u>use</u> all her money. _____

Common and proper nouns

Nouns that refer to general people, places, and things are called **common nouns**; e.g., boy, country. Nouns that refer to specific people, places, things, days, and months are called **proper nouns**. They always start with a capital letter; e.g., Leo, Japan.

1 **Shade the common nouns blue and the proper nouns red.**

dog   bee   cat

Africa   egg   wolf   Miranda

Thursday   hen   December

2 **Sort the words.**

beach	George Washington	museum	Europe
pilot	Cinderella	America	singer
library	Mr. Jones	Mount Rushmore	explorer

General people	Specific people
_____	_____
_____	_____
_____	_____

General places	Specific places
_____	_____
_____	_____
_____	_____

L.3.2 Demonstrate command of the conventions of standard English capitalization when writing.

No Problem!

Drawing conclusions
To draw conclusions from a text, use clues to make judgments. The clues help you find the answers hiding in the text.

Read the passage.

Circle the word that tells us Jack was enjoying the movie.

Highlight the word that tells what Jack's room looked like.

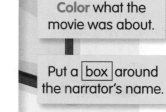

Color what the movie was about.

Put a box around the narrator's name.

Underline why Jack didn't want to turn off the television.

It was Sunday afternoon. I was in my bedroom watching a good movie about aliens when Mom poked her head in. You could tell by the look on her face that she wasn't happy.

"Just look at the state of this room, Jack," she said. "It looks like a pigsty. Turn off the television and clean it up."

"In a minute," I answered, wishing she'd go away. The aliens were about to attack Earth and I wanted to see what was going to happen.

Circle the correct answer for each question.

1 Which is the best **conclusion**? Jack was watching a ...
a comedy.   b cartoon.   c science fiction movie.   d horror movie.

2 Which word is the **clue** to question 1's answer?
a bedroom   b aliens   c good   d watching

3 Which is the best **conclusion**? Jack's room was ...
a muddy.   b spotless.   c organized.   d messy.

4 Which word is the **clue** to question 3's answer?
a pigsty   b state   c clean   d television

5 **Which phrase tells us** that the movie was at an exciting point?
a In a minute   b go away   c about to attack   d wanted to see

No Problem!

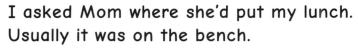

Read the passage.

Read the whole story

Put a box around who Jack asked where his lunch was.

Circle the word that suggests that Jack was in a bad mood.

> I asked Mom where she'd put my lunch. Usually it was on the bench.
>
> "Oh, I don't do lunches," Mom said. "You have to make your own sandwiches."
>
> "I'm already late," I grumbled. "You're going to have to drive me to school."
>
> Mom shook her head. "I don't think so, dear. I don't run a taxi service. You'll have to walk."
>
> Grabbing my school bag, I raced out the door. Thanks to Mom, I didn't have a hope of getting to school on time.
>
> On the way I tried to think of a good excuse to tell my teacher. I decided it was easier to tell Mr. Jones the truth.

Color the reason Jack wanted Mom to drive him to school.

Underline who Jack blamed for being late for school.

1. What can we **conclude** about who usually made Jack's lunch?

_____

2. What is the **clue** to question 1's answer?

_____

3. Why can we **conclude** that Jack had probably overslept?

_____

4. **How do we know** that Jack was going to be late for school?

_____

_____

5. Why can we **conclude** that Jack thought it was his mom's fault that he was going to be late for school?

_____

RL.3.1 Ask and answer questions to demonstrate understanding of a text, referring explicitly to the text as the basis for the answers.

shr and thr

The letter patterns **shr** and **thr** are often found at the beginning of words; e.g., **shr**ub, **thr**one.

List ① Write the word.

shred _____

three _____

shrub _____

throw _____

shrug _____

threw _____

shrill _____

throb _____

throne _____

thrill _____

shrine _____

thrive _____

shrink _____

thrash _____

throng _____

shrunk _____

thrust _____

shrimp _____

thrush _____

thresh _____

② Word clues.

Which list word means?

a short tree _____

b tomb of a saint _____

c push with force _____

d common songbird _____

e beat or pulse strongly _____

f crowd of people _____

③ Sort the words.

a *shr* words

_____ _____

_____ _____

_____ _____

_____

b *thr* words

_____ _____

_____ _____

_____ _____

_____ _____

_____ _____

④ Complete the word with *shr* or *thr*.

a ____ ____ ____ ow   b ____ ____ ____ imp   c ____ ____ ____ ush   d ____ ____ ____ one

L.3.2.F Use spelling patterns and generalizations in writing words.

9

shr and thr

1 **Revise your spelling list from page 9.** Underline the spelling mistake.
Write the word correctly.

a My shirt shrenk in the wash. _____

b We're cooking shremp for dinner. _____

c The king sat upon his throwne. _____

d I throo my sweater into my bag. _____

e We spotted a thursh high up in the tree. _____

f I covered my ears because of the boy's shrell voice. _____

g The sum of one and two is thri. _____

h I chred the paper into tiny pieces. _____

i Riding a rollercoaster is such a threll. _____

Challenge words

2 **Write the word.**

throat _____

through _____

shriek _____

thread _____

shrewd _____

throttle _____

shroud _____

shrivel _____

shrapnel _____

enthrone _____

3 **Hidden words.** Find the challenge word.

a thshrthroatthrgh _____

b shrooshrapnelshror _____

c throughshrou _____

d shrapthrottlesh _____

e hruenthrone _____

f rshrouthreadoeiu _____

g heerrshrewdasshs _____

h enthrshrivelenneeh _____

i shseeshrieksshrei _____

4 **Another way to say it.** Which challenge word could replace the underlined word?

a The girl let out a loud <u>yelp</u> of excitement. _____

b The flowers could <u>wilt</u> and die in the hot sun. _____

c My brother made a <u>clever</u> move to get closer to the cake. _____

d Tamara had a loose <u>strand</u> hanging from her coat. _____

L.3.2.F Use spelling patterns and generalizations in writing words.

Capitalization and proper nouns

Nouns that refer to specific people, places, things, days, and months are called **proper nouns**. Each word in a **proper noun** starts with a capital letter; e.g., New York City.

New York City

1 **Circle the proper nouns.**

a   My dog's name is Rover.

b   The restaurant is in Hunter Street.

c   There are many large cities in Asia.

d   I have a photo of the Statue of Liberty.

e   I watched a play at the Globe Theater.

f   We always go trick-or-treating on Halloween.

2 **Underline the proper noun that isn't capitalized. Write the word correctly.**

a   My uncle has just bought a chevrolet.   _____

b   Earth is part of the Milky Way galaxy.   _____

c   The prince's mother is queen Elizabeth.   _____

d   John lives in San diego.   _____

e   They climbed to the top of denali.   _____

f   There are many islands in the Mediterranean sea.   _____

3 **Write the names correctly.**

a   eiffel tower

b   golden gate bridge

c   central park zoo

_____   _____   _____

Kalo Li's New Country

Read the passage.

Circle the food the narrator likes best.

Highlight why the narrator likes the old people.

Color the words the narrator uses to describe the customers.

Put a box around the adjective the narrator uses to describe pork buns.

A good thing about working in the restaurant is being able to choose any dish I like. Pork buns are my favorite.

Some customers are funny and have a joke with you. Old people seem to be easier to talk to.

Others aren't so nice. When they order their food, they say things like, "No salt. No soy sauce. Be quick about it."

I'm very careful when taking down their order, so that I get it right.

Circle the correct answer for each question.

1 From the narrator's **point of view**, which is the best dish in the restaurant?
  a sweet and sour pork b pork buns c pork belly d pork spare ribs

2 How does the narrator express her **opinion** about the dish she likes most? She says ...
  a it is delicious. b it's amazing. c she loves it. d it's her favorite.

3 What is the narrator's **opinion** of the older customers? She ...
  a thinks they are funny. b doesn't like them. c likes them. d is scared of them.

4 How does the narrator express her **opinion** of the older customers? She says they ...
  a are easier to talk to. b tell funny jokes.
  c don't like salt. d are in a hurry.

5 What is the narrator's overall **opinion** of the customers?
  a She likes them all. b She doesn't like any of them.
  c Some are nice and others are not so nice. d She thinks they are rude.

RL.3.3 Describe characters in a story (e.g., their traits, motivations, or feelings) and explain how their actions contribute to the sequence of events.

Kalo Li's New Country

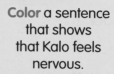
Read the whole story

Read the passage.

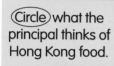
Circle what the principal thinks of Hong Kong food.

Put a box around the pronouns that show that Kalo is the narrator.

Our school had a Food Day. Mom made me some honey king prawns to take to school.

The principal was very impressed with our Hong Kong food.

On Friday, the principal said, "We're going to visit your restaurant, Kalo. My staff and I will be coming tomorrow night for dinner."

My face went red. I wondered what the principal would order. What if he didn't like the food? What if I dropped a spring roll on him? What would my principal say to Mom? I was not the best student in the school.

Color a sentence that shows that Kalo feels nervous.

Highlight what kind of a student Kalo thinks she is.

1 What was the principal's **opinion** of food from Hong Kong?

_____

2 How do we know that the events in the story are told from Kalo's **point of view**?

_____

_____

3 How does Kalo **feel** about the principal and his staff coming to visit her restaurant?

_____

_____

4 Which sentence gives the best **clue** to question 3's answer?

_____

5 What is Kalo's **opinion** of herself as a student?

_____

RL.3.3 Describe characters in a story (e.g., their traits, motivations, or feelings) and explain how their actions contribute to the sequence of events.

> Some words that end in the letters **et**, **it**, and **ot** have a similar end sound; e.g., buck**et**, rabb**it**, carr**ot**.

Endings: et, it, ot

List **①** **Write the word.**

market _____

secret _____

pocket _____

jacket _____

basket _____

planet _____

blanket _____

visit _____

rabbit _____

carrot _____

target _____

cricket _____

wallet _____

bullet _____

trumpet _____

helmet _____

submit _____

bandit _____

profit _____

② **Chunks.** Rearrange the letters to make a list word.

a rk ma et _____

b an bl ket _____

c et ck ja _____

d rr ot ca _____

e it bb ra _____

f sk ba et _____

g um tr pet _____

h lm et he _____

③ **Meaning.** Which list word means?

a A person who steals from people who are traveling

_____

b To give in _____

c When money made is more than money spent

_____

d An object an arrow is shot at _____

e A place where goods are bought and sold

_____

f Something private, not told to others

_____

④ **Complete the list words.**

a helm ____ ____

b band ____ ____

c carr ____ ____

d targ ____ ____

e rabb ____ ____

f trump ____ ____

g subm ____ ____

h crick ____ ____

⑤ **Name.**

a b c

_____ _____ _____

L.3.2.F Use spelling patterns and generalizations in writing words.

Endings: et, it, ot

1 **Revise your spelling list from page 14.** Complete each sentence with a list word.

a I put my cell phone in the _____ of my pants.

b Our _____ revolves around the sun.

c I wear a _____ when the weather is cold.

d We put the food in a picnic _____.

e The arrow just missed its _____.

f I went to the _____ to buy fruit and vegetables.

g I fed the horse a _____.

h When it is cold I put an extra _____ on my bed.

Challenge words

2 **Write the word.**

poet _____

quiet _____

diet _____

budget _____

cabinet _____

permit _____

deposit _____

inherit _____

summit _____

maggot _____

3 **Word clues.** Which challenge word means?

a a person who writes poetry

_____

b the food eaten by a person or animal

_____

c the larvae of flies and other insects

_____

d opposite to noisy

_____

e the highest part, the peak

_____

f to allow

_____

4 **Another way to say it.** Which challenge word could replace the underlined word?

a The climber reached the <u>top</u> of the mountain. _____

b Mom went to the bank to <u>put</u> money into my account. _____

c We keep our cups in the <u>cupboard</u>. _____

d Toby will <u>receive</u> the family business when his father retires. _____

e Our teacher does not <u>allow</u> talking during class. _____

Personal pronouns

A pronoun is a word that stands in place of a noun. Using pronouns means you don't have to keep repeating nouns. Use **personal pronouns** in place of the people or things; e.g., **Matt** is eating an ice cream. **He** is eating an ice cream.

1 **Circle the personal pronoun in each shape.**

a Myra **she**   b **he** Benji   c children **them**

d **it** bird   e players **we**   f parents **they**   g Max **I**

h Tina **me**   i **you** William   j **us** dancers

....

2 **Replace the underlined words with pronouns.**

Sarah dropped her pen on the floor. Ruby picked <u>the pen</u> **a** _____ up and
gave <u>the pen</u> **b** _____ back to <u>Sarah</u> **c** _____. Sarah thanked Ruby.
Sarah asked <u>Ruby</u> **d** _____ if <u>Ruby</u> **e** _____ would like to sit next to
<u>Sarah</u> **f** _____. Now <u>Sarah and Ruby</u> **g** _____ are best friends!

....

3 **Correct the word that is wrong.**

a Last week us went to Denver. _____

b Me put the books back on the shelf. _____

c Her went running early this morning. _____

d Last night him went to bed early. _____

e I gave she some of my lunch. _____

f Yesterday them finished their tasks. _____

g I told he to do his trumpet practice. _____

h I saw they at the beach. _____

i Rhys and me are going to the movies. _____

j He helped I cut out the pictures. _____

L.3.1.A Explain the function of pronouns in general and their functions in particular sentences.

The Lazy Tortoise

Read the passage.

Think marks

To understand what you are reading, you can use special marks to identify the parts you can see clearly, the parts you don't understand, and the personal connections you make to situations in the text.

If you can see question 1's answer clearly place a ☺ next to it.

If you had to look up the meaning of the word *heron*, place a **W** next to it. If you knew the meaning, place a ✓ next to it.

All the animals of the world were very excited.

"The great god Jupiter is getting married, and we're all invited to the wedding!" said a heron.

"What about me?" asked a cockroach. "Are you sure that even the small creatures are invited?"

"Yes, every one of us," replied a skink. "Jupiter said that every living creature is invited to the wedding."

Soon, an amazing swarm of living creatures began to head to the palace!

If you had to look up the meaning of the word skink, place a **W** next to it. If you knew the meaning, place a ✓ next to it.

If you can see question 4's answer place a ☺ next to it.

Draw a **chain** next to a situation you can connect to.

Circle the correct answer for each question.

1 How were all the animals of the world **feeling**?

   a happy   b excited   c confused   d sad

2 What kind of creature is a **heron**?

   a a reptile   b a marsupial   c an insect   d a bird

3 What is a **skink**?

   a a type of snake   b a type of bird   c a type of lizard   d a type of monkey

4 Where were all the creatures **going**?

   a to the palace   b to the jungle   c to the zoo   d to the park

5 Which of the following situations can most of us **connect** to?

   a going to a god's wedding   b walking with a swarm of animals

   c talking to a cockroach   d feeling excited about something

The Lazy Tortoise

Read the passage.

If you can see question 1's answer clearly place a ☺ next to it.

Place a ✓ next to question 2's answer to show that you understand that part of the text.

If you had to look up the meanings of snug and cozy, place a **W** next to the words. If you knew the answer, use a ✓ instead.

Do you understand how Jupiter punished the tortoise? If you do, place a ✓ next to the answer.

Draw a **chain** next to the part of the text that you can connect to.

Place a ✓ next to furious if you know what it means. Use a **W** if you are unsure of its meaning.

Only after the wedding, when all the guests were enjoying a feast, did the tortoise plod up to the palace. Jupiter was very annoyed.

"Why are you so late?" he demanded. "Every other creature in the world managed to be at my wedding, but not you."

"Well, I didn't want to leave my home," said the tortoise. "I was happy at home, all snug and cozy."

Jupiter was furious. The tortoise would rather be in his filthy ditch than in his royal palace!

"So it shall be!" he said. "If you love your home so much, you will carry it on your back for the rest of your life!"

1. How did Jupiter **feel** when he saw the tortoise plodding up to the palace?

_____

2. What **reason** did the tortoise give for being late? _____

_____

3. What does it mean to be **snug and cozy?** _____

_____

4. How did Jupiter **punish** the tortoise for being late? _____

_____

5. Write about a time when you had to go somewhere but would rather have stayed at home.

_____

_____

RL.3.1 Ask and answer questions to demonstrate understanding of a text, referring explicitly to the text as the basis for the answers.

Digraphs: oy, oi

> A **digraph** is two letters that make a single sound.
>
> The letters **oy** make the single sound **oy**; e.g., t**oy**, enj**oy**.
>
> The letters **oi** also make the single sound **oy**; e.g., s**oi**l, j**oi**n.

List ① Write the word.

oil _____

boy _____

boil _____

toy _____

coin _____

joy _____

soil _____

toil _____

point _____

joint _____

avoid _____

enjoy _____

noise _____

voice _____

annoy _____

royal _____

foyer _____

loyal _____

spoil _____

convoy _____

② Fill in the missing list word.

a We have to _____ the water to make spaghetti.

b The child was excited to play with his new _____.

c We really _____ going to the beach.

d My dad likes to _____ me on my birthday.

e We planted seeds in the _____.

f I put a _____ in the vending machine.

g I tried to _____ getting sunburned by putting on sunscreen.

h I like to sing in a really loud _____.

i There was a strange _____ coming from outside.

j The Queen is part of a _____ family.

k We waited in the _____ of the apartment block.

③ Fill in the missing letters.

a f ___ ___er   b l ___ ___al

c p ___ ___nt   d j ___ ___nt

e av ___ ___d   f t ___ ___l

g ann ___ ___   h ___ ___l

④ Name.

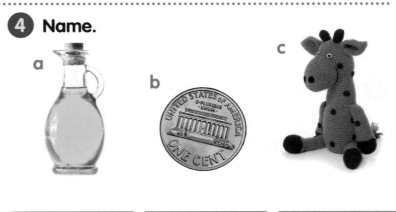

a _____ b _____ c _____

Digraphs: oy, oi

1 **Revise your spelling list on page 19.** Underline the spelling mistake. Write the word correctly.

a   He tossed his last coyn into the wishing well. _____

b   Having a weekend with Grandma in the city gave her much joi. _____

c   The workers had to toyle all day under the hot sun. _____

d   I tried to poynt the traveler in the right direction. _____

e   I kicked the ball so hard I hurt the joynt in my leg. _____

f   I tried to avoyd eating vegetables by hiding under my bed. _____

g   The lawn mower was making a terrible noyse. _____

h   I was cheering so much that I lost my voyce. _____

Challenge words

2 **Write the word.**

anoint   _____

employ   _____

choice   _____

appoint   _____

destroy   _____

poise   _____

oyster   _____

voyage   _____

poison   _____

corduroy   _____

3 **Word clues.** Which challenge word means?

a   to apply oil as part of a religious ceremony

_____

b   a long journey by land, air, or sea

_____

c   a substance that can harm, or kill

_____

d   to assign a job, role, or position

_____

e   fabric, typically used for pants

_____

f   an animal with a hard shell and soft body

_____

4 **Another way to say it.** Which challenge word could replace the underlined word?

a   It was my <u>decision</u> to stay at home. _____

b   The superhero was trying to <u>smash</u> the evil villain. _____

c   Dad had to <u>hire</u> a plumber to fix the pipes. _____

d   The explorers are planning a <u>journey</u> around the world. _____

L.3.2.F Use spelling patterns and generalizations in writing words.

Adjectives

Adjectives give information about nouns or pronouns;
e.g., the **blue** bicycle.

1 **Circle the adjectives that can describe the elephant.**

huge	small	gray	enormous
little	big	wrinkly	magnificent
tiny	heavy	large	smart

2 **Sort the adjectives.**

joyful	scared	furious	angry	happy
anxious	pleased	mad	frightened	irritated
glad	worried	cheerful	nervous	annoyed

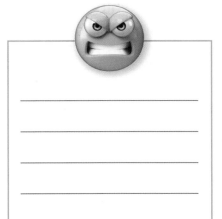

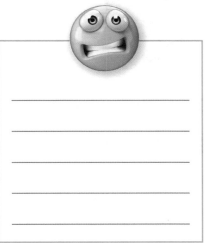

_____

_____

_____

_____

_____

3 **Complete the sentences with adjectives from the box.**

a The children laughed at the _____ clown.

b Melissa has _____ hair and _____ eyes.

c The _____ man lives in a _____ house.

d The water turned to ice in the _____ weather.

e The _____ egg has a _____ smell.

f We enjoyed eating the _____ oranges.

brown	juicy
large	funny
blue	bad
rich	rotten
freezing	

L.3.1.A Explain the function of adjectives in general and their functions in particular sentences.

21

What Kind of Pirate?

Making predictions
You can predict what is going to happen in a text based on clues in the words and pictures and what you already know.

Read the passage.

Circle a word that tells us what Captain Red Beard and his crew like to collect.

Put a box around the word that shows how Captain Red Beard and his crew get their treasure.

Underline the things Captain Red Beard and his crew like to do.

Highlight the question Captain Red Beard asks.

Color the reason Captain Red Beard gives for wanting to board the ship.

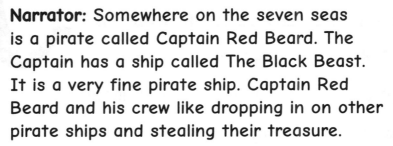

Narrator: Somewhere on the seven seas is a pirate called Captain Red Beard. The Captain has a ship called The Black Beast. It is a very fine pirate ship. Captain Red Beard and his crew like dropping in on other pirate ships and stealing their treasure.

Fingers: Pirate ship on the starboard bow, Captain.

Captain Red Beard: Good spotting, Fingers. Happy seadogs! Let's meet them.

Ahoy there fellow pirates! Can my crew and I board your ship? We could swap a few pirate tales of terror and treasure.

Circle the correct answers for each question.

1 What two **predictions** can you make about what will happen next in the story?
   a Captain Red Beard and his crew will invite the other crew onto their ship.
   b Captain Red Beard and his crew will board the pirate ship.
   c Captain Red Beard and his crew will shout louder.
   d Captain Red Beard and his crew will steal the pirates' treasure.
   e Captain Red Beard and his crew will tell the other pirates a story.

2 What **evidence** is there in the text to support your predictions? Choose three answers.
   a Captain Red Beard and his crew like dropping in on other pirate ships.
   b Captain Red Beard's ship is called The Black Beast.
   c Captain Red Beard and his crew like stealing other pirates' treasure.
   d Fingers spotted a ship on the starboard bow.
   e Captain Red Beard wants to meet the pirates on the other ship.

RL.3.1 Ask and answer questions to demonstrate understanding of a text, referring explicitly to the text as the basis for the answers.

What Kind of Pirate?

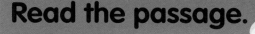

Read the passage.

Underline the adjectives Captain Red Beard uses to describe Captain Rat's crew.

Narrator: Captain Red Beard had an idea.

Captain Red Beard: Nasty? Yes, you are the nastiest pirates I have ever met. We would like to help you be nasty. You must decide on the nastiest thing you can do to us. My crew will go below decks while you have a nasty little meeting about it.

Narrator: Captain Rat thought this was a wonderfully nasty idea. His crew all argued about what was nastiest. Captain Red Beard and his crew went below.

Color two sentences that help you understand what Captain Red Beard and his crew are planning to do.

1 What **prediction** can you make about what Captain Red Beard is planning to do?

_____

_____

2 What do you know about pirates that **helped you** make your prediction?

_____

_____

3 What **prediction** can you make about what Captain Rat and his crew are going to do to Captain Red Beard and his crew?

_____

_____

4 What **evidence** is there in the text that helped you make your prediction?

_____

_____

RL.3.1 Ask and answer questions to demonstrate understanding of a text, referring explicitly to the text as the basis for the answers.

ch sound

The sound **ch** is usually spelled **tch** when it comes **after a vowel**; e.g., fe**tch**, sw**itch**.

The sound **ch** is spelled **ch** when it comes **after n**; e.g., in**ch**, hun**ch**.

List

itch

patch

catch

ditch

fetch

bench

munch

match

pitch

pinch

clutch

snatch

stitch

twitch

sketch

ranch

branch

switch

scratch

watch

1 **Write the word.**

2 **Sort the words.**

a *ch* words

b *tch* words

3 **In a group.** Write the list word that belongs in each group.

a seat, chair, _____

b draw, paint, _____

c clock, timer, _____

d stick, leaf, _____

e chew, crunch, _____

f garden, farm, _____

4 **Name.**

a _____

b _____

c _____

d _____

L.3.2.F Use spelling patterns and generalizations in writing words.

ch sound

1 **Revise your spelling list from page 24.** Underline the mistake.
Write the word correctly.

a I had an ietch I couldn't scratch. _____

b We sat on the greenest petch of grass. _____

c I told my dog to fech the ball. _____

d I like to muntch on a carrot when helping in the garden. _____

e He tried to snach the ball. _____

f Mom had to stich the hole in my jeans. _____

g I tried to cach the glass before it fell. _____

h He accidentally drove into a dich. _____

i Someone turned off the light swich. _____

Challenge words

2 **Write the word.**

wretch _____

kitchen _____

blotchy _____

butcher _____

satchel _____

quench _____

launch _____

scrunch _____

stretch _____

hatchet _____

3 **Complete the sentence.**

a Use a _____ to chop the firewood.

b At the market, I saw the _____ preparing meat.

c The scientist counted down to the rocket _____.

d I carry my books in a _____.

e The rash made her skin all _____.

f I like to _____ the fall leaves under my feet.

g You should _____ before sport.

h We cook all our food in the _____.

4 **Word clues.** Which challenge word means?

a to satisfy one's thirst _____

b someone who is very unhappy _____

c a small bag _____

Apostrophes for ownership

To make a singular noun show ownership, add an **apostrophe** (') plus **s**;
e.g., The man**'s** keys are on the table.

1 **Circle the word that shows ownership.**

a   I am in Coach Olson's team.

b   My father's tie is gray and blue.

c   The man's name is Mr. Brown.

d   That is Professor Redman's house.

e   These are Captain Westlake's orders.

f   The swimmer's trunks are in his locker.

g   Everyone admires Aunt Nada's necklace.

A (fox's) coat is reddish brown.

2 **Fill in the missing words.**

a   a _chef's_ tall hat   b   an _____ trunk   c   a _____ blowhole

3 **Fill in the words.**

a   The yolk that belongs to the egg is the _____ yolk.

b   The scarf that belongs to the woman is the _____ scarf.

c   The book that belongs to the girl is the _____ book.

d   The tooth that belongs to the shark is the _____ tooth.

e   The whistle that belongs to the boy is the _____ whistle.

f   The warren that belongs to the rabbit is the _____ warren.

g   The treasure that belongs to the pirate is the _____ treasure.

Trees

Finding facts and information
To find facts and information in a text, ask the questions **Who? What? Where? or When?** The answers can be clearly seen in the text.

Read the passage.

Color what big, flat leaves can do.

Put a box around when some deciduous trees lose their leaves.

Highlight four words that describe the size of the leaves.

Underline where holly and orange trees grow.

Circle what is often found in broadleaf evergreen tree leaves.

Highlight where new seeds come from.

Most species of tree are broadleaf trees. They often have flat, wide leaves.

Big, flat leaves can catch lots of sunlight, and they need lots of water. Some broadleaf trees are deciduous and lose their leaves in winter.

Broadleaf evergreen trees, such as holly and orange trees, grow in warmer areas. They do not lose their leaves. Broadleaf evergreen trees have thicker, waxy leaves that often contain oil. The leaves can be large, small, long, or short.

Broadleaf trees are flowering plants. New seeds grow from the flowers.

Circle the correct answer for each question.

1 **What** are the big, flat leaves of broadleaf trees able to do? Catch lots of …
   a rainwater   b insects   c seeds   d sunlight

2 **When** do deciduous trees lose their leaves?
   a in summer   b in winter   c in fall   d in spring

3 **Where** do holly and orange trees grow?
   a in warmer areas   b in cooler areas
   c in very hot areas   d in very cold areas

4 **What** do the leaves of broadleaf evergreen trees often contain?
   a fruits   b seeds   c oil   d roots

5 **Where** do the new seeds of broadleaf trees come from?
   a the stems   b the leaves   c the flowers   d the roots

Trees

Read the passage.

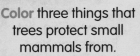

Read the
full text

(Circle) what squirrels eat.

Underline where koalas live.

Highlight where birds build their nests.

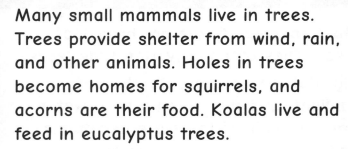

Many small mammals live in trees. Trees provide shelter from wind, rain, and other animals. Holes in trees become homes for squirrels, and acorns are their food. Koalas live and feed in eucalyptus trees.

Many birds live their lives in trees. They build their nests in the branches or hollows of trees. Trees provide fruits, nectar, and seeds for birds to eat.

Millions of insects live in trees. Many types of beetles, ants, and butterflies depend on trees for food and shelter.

Color three things that trees protect small mammals from.

Put a box around the things birds eat.

Underline examples of insects that depend on trees for food and shelter.

 What do squirrels eat? _____

 Where do koalas live? _____

 Where do birds build their nests?

_____

_____

4 **What** do birds find to eat in trees?

_____

_____

5 **What** types of insects depend on trees for food and shelter?

_____

_____

RI.3.1 Ask and answer questions to demonstrate understanding of a text, referring explicitly to the text as the basis for the answers.

Trigraphs: air, eer

A **trigraph** is three letters that make a single sound. The letters **air** make the single sound **air**; e.g., st**air**, f**air**. The letters **eer** make the single sound **ear**; e.g., d**eer**, p**eer**.

List **1** **Write the word.**

fair _____

deer _____

hair _____

peer _____

veer _____

pair _____

jeer _____

hairy _____

airy _____

chair _____

repair _____

steer _____

dairy _____

sneer _____

cheer _____

fairy _____

stair _____

lair _____

flair _____

sheer _____

2 **Fill in the missing letters.**

a re ___ ___ir

b pe ___ ___

c j ___ ___r

d d ___ i ___ y

e sn ___ ___ r

f f ___ ___ ry

g s ___ e ___ r

h st ___ ___ r

3 **Word clues.** Which list word means?

a something you sit on _____

b it grows on your head _____

c two things that are alike _____

d to fix something _____

e shout of encouragement _____

f made from milk _____

g to move in a certain direction _____

4 **Name.**

a _____ b _____ c _____ d _____

L.3.2.F Use spelling patterns and generalizations in writing words.

29

Trigraphs: air, eer

1 **Revise your spelling list from page 29.** Underline the spelling mistakes.
Write the word correctly.

a   The judge wanted to give him a feir trial.   _____

b   The deir had two large antlers.   _____

c   I apologized when I realized my jeir had hurt his feelings.   _____

d   That hole in the ground is a fox's leir.   _____

e   The captain had to steir the ship into the harbor.   _____

f   The cows were raised on a deiry farm.   _____

g   The giant spider in my room had eight long and heiry legs.   _____

h   She has a fleir for dancing.   _____

i   My brother almost tripped on the top steir.   _____

Challenge words

2 **Write the word.**

pioneer   _____

mountaineer   _____

staircase   _____

eerie   _____

engineer   _____

volunteer   _____

despair   _____

career   _____

fairly   _____

mohair   _____

3 **Complete the sentence.**

a   Ali wanted a _____ in medicine.

b   The _____ drew maps of the undiscovered land.

c   Her sweater was made from _____.

d   We walked up the _____.

4 **Hidden words.** Find the challenge word.

a   omtamountaineerin   _____

b   eeirieerieieirie   _____

c   lyairffairlyiraf   _____

d   ohmirmohairirhmo   _____

e   oinpepioneeriopner   _____

5 **Word clues.** Which challenge word means?

a   the first to explore something unknown   _____

b   a mountain climber   _____

c   weird and frightening   _____

L.3.2.F Use spelling patterns and generalizations in writing words.

Action verbs

An **action verb** tells us what action is happening; e.g., They **jump** up and down. Remember verbs must agree with their subjects; e.g., She **jumps** up and down.

1 **Circle the word that shows what action is happening in each sentence.**

a   Marcus throws the ball.

b   Gina catches the ball.

c   Kai eats his dinner.

d   Frieda drinks her juice.

e   Elena drops the plate.

f   George cleans the mess

g   The boys play games.

h   The girls read books.

i   The man drives the car.

j   The cyclists ride their bikes.

2 **Fill in the verbs.**

> escapes   crumples   pays   wags
> brushes   puts   squawk

a   The seagulls _____ loudly.

b   The prisoner _____ from jail.

c   Rosie's mother _____ her hair.

d   The child _____ his rubbish in the trash can.

e   The boy _____ the paper into a ball.

f   The customer _____ in the store.

g   My dog _____ his tail when he is happy.

3 **Match the verbs.**

a   rains   sketches

b   cry   stroll

c   walk   weep

d   looks   protects

e   draws   drizzles

f   chew   cleans

g   sleeps   screams

h   washes   munch

i   shouts   peers

j   guards   dozes

4 **Choose the correct verb.**

a   Jack and Jill (go, goes) _____ up the hill.

b   Humpty Dumpty (sit, sits) _____ on the wall.

c   Cinderella (dance, dances) _____ with the prince.

d   The three bears (find, finds) _____ Goldilocks in their house.

L.3.1.A Explain the function of verbs in general and their functions in particular sentences.

31

Plants as Food

Compare and contrast
To compare and contrast information, look for the similarities and differences between details in the text.

Read the passage.

Highlight the words *peaches* and *cherries*. **Color** the key words that tell us how they are similar.

Circle the words that tell about the kind of weather raspberries and apples prefer.

Stone fruits, fruits with pits, also grow on trees. They have one hard seed covered with soft flesh. Peaches, plums, cherries, and apricots are stone fruits.

Many fruits are quite small. Strawberries, raspberries, and blackberries are all small fruits with lots of seeds. They grow on small plants or bushes in cool areas.

Apples and pears grow on trees in cool areas. They both have a core with small seeds inside. Some apples are grown to make juice to drink.

Put boxes around the information about the seeds in peaches and in pears.

Underline the words that tell what kind of plants strawberries and blackberries grow on.

Carefully read the following sentences. Put a T next to the statements that are true, and an F next to the statements that are false.

1. [ ] Peaches and pears have the same number of seeds.

2. [ ] Peaches and pears grow on trees.

3. [ ] Cherries and strawberries are fruits.

4. [ ] Cherries and strawberries are both stone fruits.

5. [ ] Raspberries and apples prefer cooler weather.

6. [ ] Raspberries and apples are both small fruits.

7. [ ] Strawberries and blackberries grow on small plants or bushes.

Plants as Food

Read the passage.

Circle the key word that shows how honey and sugar are similar.

Underline what herbs and spices are used for.

Color the words that tell how chocolate and vanilla are similar.

Many animals have a "sweet tooth." Birds and bees drink sweet nectar from flowers, and bears eat honey. People eat sugar made from the dried juice of sugar cane.

Herbs and spices are used in cooking. Herbs such as basil and parsley are used as seasoning. Garlic adds flavor, and chilies are hot and spicy.

Chocolate, vanilla, and cinnamon are also plant flavors. Chocolate is made from seeds. Vanilla is made from seed pods, and cinnamon is ground from the dried bark of a tree.

Many drinks are made using plants. Coffee beans and tea leaves both come from plants. Lemonade is made from the juice of lemons.

Put a box around the sentence that shows how garlic and chilies are different.

Highlight the difference between chocolate and vanilla.

Circle two ways in which tea and coffee are similar.

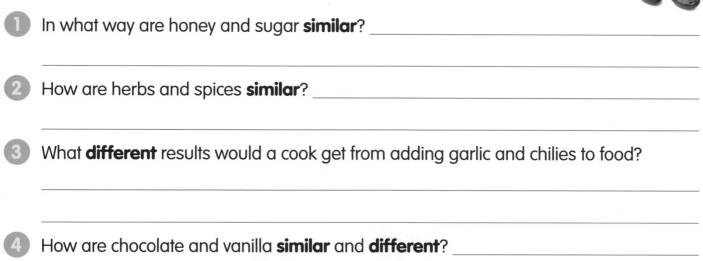

1. In what way are honey and sugar **similar**? _____

_____

2. How are herbs and spices **similar**? _____

_____

3. What **different** results would a cook get from adding garlic and chilies to food?

_____

_____

4. How are chocolate and vanilla **similar** and **different**? _____

_____

_____

5. List two **similarities** between coffee and tea. _____

_____

Plurals: s, es

You make most plurals by adding **s** to singular nouns; e.g., 1 town → 2 town**s**. For nouns that end in **s**, **sh**, **ch**, **x** and **z**, add **es**; e.g., 4 bus**es**, 3 wish**es**, 2 watch**es**, 5 box**es**. Some nouns that end in **o** have **es** in the plural; e.g., 10 potato**es**.

List **1** **Write the word.**

bats _____

foxes _____

socks _____

pianos _____

birds _____

buses _____

dishes _____

tomatoes _____

mixes _____

buzzes _____

towers _____

bushes _____

skills _____

mouths _____

punches _____

packets _____

wishes _____

silks _____

echoes _____

marches _____

2 **Complete the table.**

Singular	Plural
sock	
bus	
wish	
bird	
	foxes
	mouths
packet	
	tomatoes
piano	
dish	

3 **Unscramble these list words.**

a wersto _____ b oxsef _____

c unchpes _____ d matoesto _____

e anpios _____ f irbds _____

g archems _____ h zzbues _____

i ochese _____ j lksis _____

k ackpets _____ l outhms _____

4 **Name.**

a _____ b _____ c _____ d _____

L.3.2.E Use conventional spelling for high-frequency and other studied words and for adding suffixes to base words.

Plurals: s, es

1 **Revise your spelling list from page 34.**
Write the list word that belongs in each group.

a shoes, laces, _____

b feathers, nests, _____

c carrots, onions, _____

d violins, drums, _____

e balls, rackets, _____

f trains, cars, _____

2 **Fill in the missing letters.**

a march_____

b buzz_____

c packet_____

d echo_____

e skill_____

f wish_____

g mix_____

h punch_____

Challenge words

3 **Write the word.**

peaches _____

crosses _____

sopranos _____

tattoos _____

churches _____

stretchers _____

coaches _____

houses _____

superheroes _____

slippers _____

4 **Complete the sentence.**

a Our football team has two _____ this season.

b We bought a box of juicy _____ at the market.

c I wear my _____ to keep my feet warm.

d We put on temporary _____ at the fair.

e The _____ in the choir sing the high notes.

f My favorite stories are about _____.

5 **Word clues.** Which challenge word means?

a fruit _____

b warm shoes _____

c places of worship _____

d superhumans _____

e places you live _____

6 **Hidden words.** Find the challenge word.

a hhcoacoachescce _____

b chterstretchersthce _____

c ssoesccrossesrross _____

d ottostattoosattos _____

e oushhouseshos _____

L.3.2.E Use conventional spelling for high-frequency and other studied words and for adding suffixes to base words.

Capital letters in direct speech

The **first word** someone says in direct speech starts with a **capital letter**; e.g., Marlene said, "**P**lease pass the salt."

If the same person speaks a second time, the first word starts with a capital letter **only** if it comes **after a full stop**, e.g., "My favorite food is pasta," said Megan. "**W**hat's yours?"

"My favorite food is pasta," said Megan, "**b**ut I also like fried rice."

1 **Tick the sentences that have the correct punctuation.**

a   Ravi said, "My best friends' names are Max and Benjamin."

b   Bianca said, "my friend and I are going to the beach this afternoon."

c   "I can reach the bottom shelf," said Tanya, "but not the top shelf."

d   "I like adventure stories," said Miles, "And I like fantasy stories."

e   "I'm going for a run," said Dad. "Would you like to join me?"

f   "I've been to Mexico many times," said Suzy. "have you ever been there?"

2 **Circle all the words that need capital letters in the following sentences.**

a   "why is snuffles barking?" asked simon.

b   georgia said, "perhaps he wants some attention."

c   "perhaps," said zoe, "but he might also be hungry."

d   "dad fed him an hour ago," said annabel.

e   "he's been barking a lot lately. maybe we should give him more attention."

3 **What could each of these people be saying?**

a The doctor said, _____

_____

_____

_____

b The librarian said, _____

_____

_____

_____

L.3.2 Demonstrate command of the conventions of standard English capitalization, punctuation, and spelling when writing.

Grasslands

Read the passage.

Underline what forms when too little rain falls.

Color what forms when lots of rain falls.

Grasslands are environments in which grass is the main plant, rather than shrubs or trees.

Grasslands need 10 to 40 inches of rain each year. If they get less than this, they turn into deserts. If grasslands get much more rain, lots of trees grow and they become forests.

There are two main types of grassland — savannas (also called tropical grasslands) and temperate grasslands.

Put a box around the amount of rainfall grasslands need each year.

Circle the correct answer for each question.

1 What **causes** deserts to form?

a hot weather   b fires   c not enough rain   d too much rain

2 What is the **effect** on the environment when too little rain falls?

a It turns into tropical grasslands.   b It turns into forests.
c It turns into temperate grasslands.   d It turns into deserts.

3 What **causes** forests to form?

a a high rainfall   b a low rainfall   c snow and ice   d flooding rivers

4 What is the **effect** on the environment when it rains a lot?

a Deserts form.   b Forests form.   c Mountains form.   d Rivers form.

5 What type of environment do we get when an area receives between 10 to 40 inches of rain a year?

a deserts   b forests   c grasslands   d mountains

RI.3.3 Describe the relationship between a series of historical events, scientific ideas or concepts, or steps in technical procedures in a text, using language that pertains to time, sequence, and cause/effect.

Grasslands

Read the passage.

Read the full text

Grasslands

Circle the cause of the grasses dying off.

Color the effect the hot winds have on the grasses.

Underline why many animals migrate in the dry season.

Put a box around what happens when the waterholes dry up.

Highlight the reason the grasses don't completely die off.

Color the reason the grasses start growing again.

The African savanna has cycles of dry and wet seasons.

1 Dry season

Hot winds begin to blow. Grasses die off at the surface, but the roots remain alive. Fires may burn whole areas. Waterholes dry up, causing many animals to migrate. There are often violent thunderstorms before the wet season starts.

2 Wet season

When the rain starts, grass can grow 1 inch in one day.

1 What **causes** grasses on the African savanna to die off?

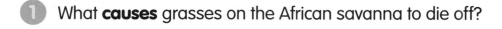

2 What **effect** do hot winds have on the African savanna?

3 **Why** do many animals migrate in the dry season?

4 **What happens** when the waterholes dry up?

5 What **causes** the grass to start growing again?

RI.3.3 Describe the relationship between a series of historical events, scientific ideas or concepts, or steps in technical procedures in a text, using language that pertains to time, sequence, and cause/effect.

Silent b, l, h

> **Silent letters** are letters in a word that are not pronounced. The letter **b** is silent when it comes **after m** or **before t**; e.g., clim**b**, de**b**t. Sometimes the letter **l** is silent when it **comes after the vowels a, o, and ou**; e.g., ca**l**f, fo**l**k, shou**l**d. The letter **h** is sometimes silent at the beginning of a word or <u>syllable</u>; e.g., **h**our, ex<u>h</u>aust.

List **1** **Write the word.**

lamb _____

limb _____

walk _____

bomb _____

calf _____

talk _____

hour _____

numb _____

comb _____

palm _____

crumb _____

should _____

could _____

climb _____

thumb _____

yolk _____

tomb _____

chalk _____

honest _____

half _____

2 **Sort the list words.**

Silent *b*	Silent *l*	Silent *h*

3 **In a group.** Write the list word that belongs in each group.

a sheep, ram, _____

b chat, conversation, _____

c egg, shell, _____

d true, genuine, _____

e second, minute, _____

f fingers, hand, _____

4 **Name.**

a _____   b _____   c _____   d _____

L.3.2.F Use spelling patterns and generalizations in writing words.

39

Silent b, l, h

1 **Revise your spelling list from page 39.** Underline the mistakes.
Write the word correctly.

a I coud not believe I won the race! _____

b I shoud have finished my library book last night. _____

c The ancient pharaoh was buried in a golden tom. _____

d It's hard to com my curly hair. _____

e I felt num after swimming in the cold water. _____

f There is only an our until the movie starts. _____

g We hung the swing from the lim of the tree. _____

Challenge words

2 **Write the word.**

would _____

exhaust _____

folk _____

heir _____

plumber _____

salmon _____

debt _____

doubt _____

honor _____

shepherd _____

3 **Complete the sentence.**

a The prince is the _____ to the throne.

b We hired a _____ to fix our kitchen sink.

c It is an _____ to receive a medal.

d Running may _____ your energy.

e The _____ had a small flock of sheep.

f They decided they _____ order pizza.

g I _____ he has a pet tiger.

h I paid off my _____.

i That story is just an old _____ tale.

j Dad went fishing and caught a huge _____.

4 **Word clues.** Which challenge
word means?

a fish _____

b broken pipe _____

c money _____

d sheep _____

5 **Hidden words.** Find the challenge word.

a auseexhausthaust _____

b oidudsbtdodoubt _____

c onhonorhorueor _____

d ldowwouldllddw _____

e eeirheireerihie _____

L.3.2.F Use spelling patterns and generalizations in writing words.

Noun phrases

A phrase is a part of a sentence that has more than one word.
A **noun phrase** is the group of words that is built around a **noun**.
It can include articles, pronouns, adjectives, and other phrases;
e.g., **an enormous giant with a bushy black beard**.

1 **Complete these noun phrases with words from the box.**

a   a herd _____ elephants

b   _____ office in the city

c   the stain _____ his shirt

d   _____ little round buttons

e   a big black _____ white dog

on	and
of	an
several	

2 **Build phrases around the following nouns.** Use the words in the boxes.

a   orange   _____

b   balloons   _____

c   box   _____

d   glass   _____

e   clown   _____

(big a juicy)   (pink several blue and)   (candy delicious a of big)

(ice a fruit cold juice of)   (nose funny the red with the)

3 **Find the noun around which each phrase is built.**

a   I ate <u>the cupcake with pink frosting</u>.   _____

b   <u>The big black dog</u> is barking at us.   _____

c   <u>The cookies in the jar</u> are delicious.   _____

d   I gave Jack <u>a big bowl of tomato soup</u>.   _____

e   She is reading <u>the postcard from her cousin</u>.   _____

f   <u>The three children in the corner</u> are reading.   _____

g   <u>The little boat on the lake</u> is bobbing up and down.   _____

L.3.1.A Explain the function of nouns in general and their functions in particular sentences.

41

Hoaxes, Fibs, and Fakes

Word study
You can often use clues in the text to help you work out the meaning of words you do not understand.

Read the passage.

(Circle) the word that tells us where the farmers got the spaghetti from.

Underline how many people did not know where spaghetti came from in the 1950's.

Color the word that tells us what nationality the farmers were.

Highlight the sentence that tells us why many English people believed the April Fools' joke.

On April Fools' Day in 1957, an English TV program showed Swiss farmers picking spaghetti from trees. Hundreds of people called the TV station and asked how to grow spaghetti trees. They were told to "place a **sprig** of spaghetti in a can of tomato sauce and hope for the best."

Because spaghetti was an **exotic** food in England at that time, many people didn't know where it came from. They believed that it could grow on trees!

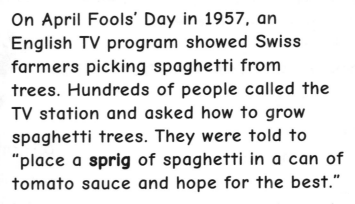

Circle the correct answer for each question.

1 Some people in England wanted to grow their own spaghetti trees. A tree is a type of ...

   a animal.   **b** plant.   **c** rock.   **d** soil.

2 Based on question 1's answer, we can infer that the word **sprig** most likely means ...

   a tail.   **b** string.   **c** stem.   **d** ribbon.

3 In the 1950's, how many people in England did not know where spaghetti came from?

   a very few   **b** one or two   **c** everyone   **d** many

4 In the TV program, who was picking spaghetti from the trees?

   a English farmers   **b** local farmers   **c** Swiss farmers   **d** children

5 Based on question 3 and 4's answers, we can infer that the word **exotic** most likely means ...

   a from a foreign country.   **b** from the same country.

   c from the earth.   **d** from a factory.

L.3.4.A Use sentence-level context as a clue to the meaning of a word or phrase.

Hoaxes, Fibs, and Fakes

Read the passage.

Circle three words that can help us work out what an astronomer does.

Underline words that can help us work out what gravity is.

> We often believe things we read, especially things that sound scientific. On 1 April 1976, **astronomer** Patrick Moore announced that Pluto would pass behind Jupiter. He said that this would lessen the **gravity** on Earth. If people jumped in the air at the exact moment the planets were in line, they would be able to float — just like astronauts in space. Some people said they had floated up to the ceiling!

1 What does an **astronomer** do? _____

_____

2 If you didn't know the answer to question 1, which words would have **helped you** work out the meaning of the word?

_____

_____

3 Which **clues** in the text can help you work out the meaning of the word **gravity**?

_____

_____

4 Now write a **definition** for the word **gravity**. _____

_____

5 What does an **astronaut** do? _____

_____

L.3.4.A Use sentence-level context as a clue to the meaning of a word or phrase.

43

Suffix: ing

> A **suffix** is added to the end of a word to make a new word with a slightly different meaning.
>
> When the suffix **ing** is added to a verb, it shows that something is still happening; e.g., dream**ing**, eat**ing**.
>
> When the verb ends in **e**, drop the **e** before adding **ing**; e.g., smil**e** → smil**ing**, rid**e** → rid**ing**.

List **① Write the word.**

mixing _____

eating _____

panting _____

asking _____

trying _____

lending _____

sleeping _____

washing _____

dreaming _____

painting _____

carrying _____

selling _____

falling _____

roaring _____

pouring _____

moving _____

hoping _____

baking _____

wiping _____

ruling _____

② Complete the sentence with a list word.

a To make money I am _____ my old bike.

b Rain is _____ from the sky.

c Nick was _____ the flour and eggs together.

d Ting is _____ a picture of her dog.

e She is _____ juice into her cup.

f I was _____ mom would make us pancakes, but she boiled eggs instead.

g Mom is _____ a chocolate cake for my birthday.

h We heard the lion _____ from its cage.

③ Fill in the missing letters.

a r ___a ___ing

b le _____ing

c ___ant _____g

d _____eep _____g

e as _____g

f ca _____y _____g

g tr _____ng

h pai _____ng

④ Word building. Add suffixes to build words.

	ing	d/ed
paint		
pour		
roar		
dream		

	ing	d/ed
ask		
bake		
wipe		
hope		

L.3.2.E Use conventional spelling for high-frequency and other studied words and for adding suffixes to base words.

Suffix: ing

1 **Revise your spelling list from page 44.** Underline the spelling mistakes.
Write the list word correctly.

a The dog was pannting in the heat. _____

b Tomorrow we are mooving from the country to the city. _____

c It is difficult ruleing a margin without a ruler. _____

d I am always lennding my books, but I never get them back. _____

e I got excited when I heard the lion roarring. _____

f My brother is always assking for more candy. _____

Challenge words

2 **Write the word.**

teasing _____

scaring _____

blaming _____

smiling _____

snoring _____

crossing _____

spraying _____

praising _____

freezing _____

whining _____

3 **Complete the sentence.**

a The bear story was s_____ the children.

b Miles is always b_____ others for his mistakes.

c Dad was s_____ like a tractor.

d We look both ways before c_____ the road.

e Max got in trouble for t_____ his sister.

f It was f_____ cold outside in winter.

4 **Hidden words.** Find the challenge word.

a irpapraisingainpr _____

b ryasprayingygns _____

c hwinwhininghing _____

d msilssmilingsim _____

5 **Another way to say it.** Which challenge word could replace the underlined word?

a The thunder was <u>frightening</u> the dog. _____

b My brother is always <u>complaining</u>. _____

L.3.2.E Use conventional spelling for high-frequency and other studied words and for adding suffixes to base words.

45

Linking verbs

> Linking verbs **do not express an action**. They link the subject to a noun or adjective in a sentence. We can call them 'being' and 'having' verbs. 'Being' verbs show that **people or things exist**; e.g., He **is** a boy. They **are** big. 'Having' verbs show **what people or things have**; e.g., She **has** a cat. They **have** four dogs.

1 Circle the 'being' and 'having' verbs in the following pairs.

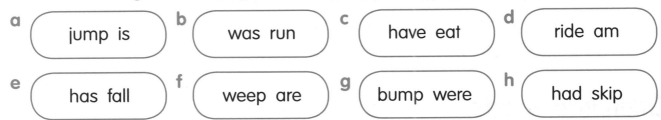

a jump is   b was run   c have eat   d ride am

e has fall   f weep are   g bump were   h had skip

2 Fill in the linking verbs.

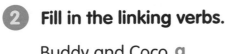

Buddy and Coco **a** _____ best friends.

Buddy **b** _____ floppy ears, but Coco's

stand up straight. They **c** _____ very

good, but they often get up to mischief. Buddy's

coat **d** _____ longer than Coco's.

They both **e** _____ the cutest

little faces!

seem	have	are
	is	has

3 Choose the right linking verb.

a The bird (is/are) _____ a bright color.

b Some animals (is/are) _____ bigger than others.

c My friend (has/have) _____ two very big dogs.

d Our neighbors (has/have) _____ a pool in their yard.

e My older brother (was/were) _____ at the skate park.

f The passengers (was/were) _____ in their cabins.

L.3.1.A Explain the function of verbs in general and their functions in particular sentences.

Spelling

Use this review to test your knowledge. It has three parts—**Spelling**, **Grammar**, and **Comprehension**. If you're unsure of an answer, go back and read the rules and generalizations in the blue boxes.

You have learned about:

- vowel sounds
- digraphs: oy, oi
- plurals: s, es

- shr and thr
- ch sound
- silent b, l, h

- endings: et, it, ot
- trigraphs: air, eer
- suffix: ing

1 **In each sentence, the spelling error has been <u>underlined</u>. Write the correct spelling.** 2 marks

a The recipe says to <u>chred</u> the lettuce _____

b "Can you keep a <u>secrit</u>?" asked my sister. _____

c Queen Elizabeth is the head of the British <u>roial</u> family. _____

d There was a loud <u>noyse</u> as Mom started the mower. _____

2 **Which word correctly completes this sentence?** 1 mark

We cooked _____, garlic, and herbs to make a yummy pasta sauce.

a tomato   b tomatos   c tomatoes   d omates

3 **This sentence has one word that is incorrect. Write the correct spelling.** 1 mark

"Dad, my new sneakers pintch my toes!" _____

4 **Write the vowels to correctly complete these words.** 2 marks

a fr ____ g   b gl ____ d   c nam ____   d pl ____ me

5 **Circle the correct verb to complete each sentence.** 3 marks

a This week we're (paint, paints, painting) landscapes.

b One day I want to (climb, climbs, climbing) Mt. Everest.

c Next year we're (move, moves, moving) to San Francisco for my mom's work.

6 **Which word correctly completes this sentence?** 1 mark

A _____ produces milk which is used to make cheese, yogurt, and ice cream.

a dairy   b deery   c dairy's   d dairies

Your score

☐

10

47

Grammar

You have learned about:

- common and proper nouns
- adjectives
- direct speech
- capital letters
- apostrophes
- noun phrases
- pronouns
- action verbs
- linking verbs

1 **In each sentence, color the common noun and underline the proper noun.** 2 marks

   a The little girl is looking for Sam.

   b My best friend comes from Canada.

2 **In each sentence, circle the words that need a capital letter.** 2 marks

   a Last summer we spent a week in new york.

   b He has two sisters called ruby and janey.

3 **Circle the pronouns that correctly complete each sentence.** 2 marks

   a Jackson said (he, him) would help (she, her).

   b (We, Us) are going to visit (they, them).

4 **Complete each sentence with an adjective from the box.** 3 marks

funny delicious six orange cold ancient

   a At the zoo, we counted _____ elephants.

   b The clown told us a _____ joke.

   c My grandmother baked us some _____ cookies.

   d The girl was wearing an _____ dress.

   e In Europe, we visited some _____ ruins.

   f The _____ weather is making me shiver.

5 **In each sentence, fill in the missing apostrophe.** 2 marks

   a Olivias book is on one of those shelves.

   b I put two potatoes on my little brothers plate.

   c The babys toys are in the cupboard.

   d The citys streets were packed with tourists.

Grammar

6 **Draw lines to match the animal to the action verb.** 3 marks

a   Horses   roar.

b   Dogs   hop.

c   Rabbits   hum.

d   Lions   gallop.

e   Snakes   bark.

f   Bees   slither.

7 **In the following sentences, circle the words that need a capital letter.** 2 marks

a   Dad shouted, "be careful!"

b   The librarian said, "please help me with these books."

c   Marty asked, "what time does the game start?"

d   Grandpa replied, "i'm not sure when it will start."

8 **Circle the noun around which each phrase is built.** 2 marks

a   the dense forest beside the river

b   a large house with a tin roof

c   the cute kitten in the picture

d   the silver cup on the table

9 **Circle the verbs in the following sentences.** 2 marks

a   The children are happy.

b   The man is at work.

c   I am taller than Joe.

d   She was in her room.

Your score

20

The Tiger, the Man, and the Jackal

Read the passage and then use the comprehension skills you have learned to answer the questions.

A tiger once got caught in a cage. He asked a man passing by to free him. At first the man refused, worried the tiger would devour him. The tiger promised that he would do no such thing. The man felt sorry for the tiger and set him free. Immediately the tiger pounced on the man.

"What a fool you are!" said the tiger. "You will make a fine meal!"

The man pleaded for his life, reminding the tiger of his promise.

"Very well," said the tiger. "If you can find someone who thinks I'm being unfair, I'll spare you."

The man told his story to a tree, a road and a water buffalo. Not one of them thought the tiger was being unfair.

The man was beginning to give up hope when he met a jackal. The man told the jackal his story.

"I don't understand," said the jackal. "I need to see where this happened."

The man took the jackal to the place where the tiger waited. The savage creature was sharpening his claws, eager to start his meal. The tiger agreed that the man could tell his story one more time.

The jackal pretended that he didn't understand a word the man was saying. Eventually the tiger lost his patience.

"Look here, you silly jackal! This is how it happened! I was in the cage..." explained the tiger as he stepped inside the cage.

Immediately the crafty jackal closed the door. Once again the tiger was trapped, but this time, the man knew better than to free him.

The Tiger, the Man, and the Jackal

1 Why did the man free the tiger? 1 mark **LITERAL**
   a The tiger promised to reward the man.   b The man felt sorry for the tiger.
   c The tiger was badly injured.   d The man was not afraid of tigers.

2 Which words best describe the man? 1 mark **CRITICAL**
   a kind and trusting   b kind and proud
   c kind and clever   d kind and fast

3 Give a text clue to support your answer to question 2. 2 marks **CRITICAL**

_____

_____

4 What was the tiger's opinion of the man? The tiger thought the man was ... 1 mark **INFERENTIAL**
   a brave.   b clumsy.   c foolish.   d kind.

5 Give a text clue to support your answer to question 4. 2 marks **CRITICAL**

_____

_____

6 Which word best describes the tiger? 1 mark **INFERENTIAL**
   a untrustworthy   b trustworthy   c fair   d patient

7 How did the jackal help the man? 1 mark **CRITICAL**
   a by defeating the tiger in a fight   b by frightening the tiger
   c by chasing the tiger away   d by tricking the tiger

8 What is the main message of this story? 1 mark **LITERAL**
   a Do not trust a jackal.
   b Kindness is not always rewarded.
   c Tigers are savage animals.
   d Stay away from cages.

Your score

☐ / 10

Your Review 1 Scores

Spelling		Grammar	Comprehension		Total
☐	+	☐	+ ☐	=	☐
10		20	10		40

Cinquains

Visualization
Visualizing the people, places, things, and events you are reading about helps build better understanding of the text. Looking for key words in the text will help you create images that match the text.

Read the poems.

In Poem 1, (circle) the words that helped you see what was happening in the tree.

1. Tree
Giant, strong
Climbing, swinging, playing
Fun among the branches
Oak

3. Spider
Hairy, hidden
Seeing, watching, knowing
Waits with all patience
Strikes

In Poem 2, **color** the words that helped you see what the spaghetti looked like on the fork.

2. Spaghetti
Loopy, meaty
Slurping, slipping, twisting
Between my fork and mouth
Yum

In Poem 3, underline the words that helped you see what the spider was doing.

1 Read each of the poems again. As you do so, visualize what you are reading about. Draw a picture for each poem.

Poem 1	Poem 3

Poem 2

RL.3.1 Ask and answer questions to demonstrate understanding of a text, referring explicitly to the text as the basis for the answers.

Cinquains

Read the poems.

1.
Zebra
Black and white stripes
Grazing on shrubs and leaves
Sudden snorts, the smell of lion
Run!

Circle the words that tell you what the zebra looked like.

Highlight the words that helped you see why the zebra ran.

2.
Balloons
Pink, white and blue
Bobbing in the garden
Happy children eating, playing
Party!

Underline the words that tell you where the balloons were.

Put a box around the words that helped you see what the children were doing.

3.
New shoes
Shiny, squeaky
Stepping, striding, stomping
Hurting my heels, pinching my toes
Ouch!

Color the words that helped you see how the shoes moved.

Circle the words that helped you visualize how the person wearing the shoes felt.

1. Read each of the poems again. As you do so, visualize what you are reading about. Draw a picture for each poem.

Poem 1

Poem 2

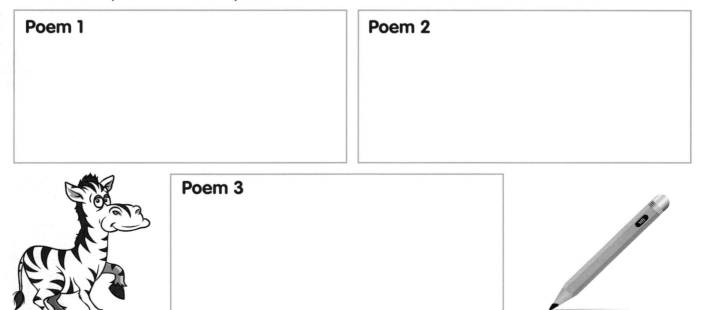

Poem 3

RL.3.1 Ask and answer questions to demonstrate understanding of a text, referring explicitly to the text as the basis for the answers.

53

Trigraph: igh

> A **trigraph** is three letters that make a single sound.
>
> The letters **igh** are a trigraph and make the long vowel sound **i**; e.g., s**igh**t, fr**igh**t.

List **1** **Write the word.**

high _____

sigh _____

nigh _____

fight _____

night _____

right _____

sight _____

tight _____

might _____

light _____

alight _____

thigh _____

mighty _____

flight _____

slight _____

bright _____

delight _____

alright _____

fright _____

knight _____

2 **Word clues.** Which list word means?

a   a medieval soldier _____

b   great happiness, or joy _____

c   the action of flying _____

d   fear or terror _____

e   the ability to see _____

f   between hip and knee _____

3 **Opposites.** Find the opposites.

a   low _____

b   day _____

c   left _____

d   loose _____

e   dark _____

f   dim _____

4 **Unscramble the words.**

a   ghribt _____

b   sghi _____

c   ghfit _____

d   nghi _____

e   ghitn _____

f   ghtri _____

5 **Missing letters.** Fill in the missing letters.

a   m ___ ___ h ___ ___

b   de ___ ___ ___ ___ ___

c   a ___ ri ___ ___ t

d   sl ___ ___ ___ t

e   f ___ i ___ ___ t

f   n ___ ___ ___ t

L.3.2.F Use spelling patterns and generalizations in writing words.

Trigraph: igh

1 **Revise your spelling list from page 54.** Underline the mistakes.
Write the word correctly.

a The bird sat hii in the tree. _____

b We always phight over the remote. _____

c Do we turn left or ryght? _____

d The sky was alyte with fireworks. _____

e We heard a myghty roar from the lion's cage. _____

f It mite rain today. _____

g The time to leave is nie. _____

h He gave a shigh of relief. _____

Challenge words

2 **Write the word.**

height _____

eyesight _____

firelight _____

insight _____

frighten _____

midnight _____

copyright _____

plight _____

weeknight _____

righteous _____

3 **Word clues.** Which challenge word means?

a light cast from a fire _____

b twelve o'clock at night _____

c a weekday night _____

d ability to see _____

e how tall _____

f to scare _____

g morally right _____

h an unhappy situation _____

i protection of one's work _____

j the power to understand _____

4 **Complete the sentence.**

a Her _____ is five foot three.

b Wednesday is my favorite _____ because I have karate practice.

c You need glasses if you have poor _____.

d The author protected her work with _____.

L.3.2.F Use spelling patterns and generalizations in writing words.

Past and present tense

The tense of a verb tells when an action takes place. **Present tense** verbs show that the action takes place now. **Past tense** verbs show that the action has already taken place; e.g., She **runs** away. She **ran** away.

1 **Write the verbs in the past tense.**

a thank _____

b push _____

c spell _____

d blink _____

e glow _____

f flap _____

g skip _____

h find _____

i feel _____

j grow _____

k think _____

l swim _____

2 **Sort the verbs.**

Present tense		**Past tense**
_____	brought speak	_____
_____	slipped trotted	_____
_____	fries pulled said	_____
_____	dug bleed dances	_____
_____	reads stops	_____
_____		_____

3 **Circle the incorrect verb. Write the word in the correct tense.**

a I puts the books back on the shelf.   _____

b Yesterday I fall and skinned my knee.   _____

c I tell her an hour ago to tidy her room.   _____

d Earlier today I write a story for my dad.   _____

e Last year they teach us how to care for our pets.   _____

f Last night she was cold, so she close the window.   _____

The North Wind and the Sun

Finding the main idea and supporting details
The main idea of a text is its key point. It sums up what the text is about. Details in the text can help you identify the main idea.

Read the passage.

Underline the sentence that best expresses the main idea of the text.

Highlight the sentence that supports the main idea.

The Wind and the Sun had a competition to see who could make the man take off his coat. The Wind began to blow as hard as he could. He blew directly on the man with a whipping, punching wind. The man became cold and wrapped his coat closely around his body. No matter how hard the Wind blew, it was useless—the man only held his coat more tightly.

Put a box around a sentence that shows what effect the Wind had on the man.

Circle the correct answer/s for each question.

1 Which sentence best expresses the **main idea** of the text?

a   The Wind tried hard to frighten the man.

b   The Wind tried hard to make the man take off his coat.

c   The Wind tried hard to make the man hold on to his coat.

d   The Wind tried hard to make the man cold.

2 Which **three details** support the main idea?

a   The Wind whipped and punched around the man.

b   The man became cold.

c   The Wind blew directly on the man.

d   The man wrapped his coat closely around his body.

e   The man held his coat more tightly.

f   The Wind blew as hard as he could.

RL.3.2 Recount stories, including fables, folktales, and myths from diverse cultures; determine the central message, lesson, or moral and explain how it is conveyed through key details in the text.

57

The North Wind and the Sun

Read the passage.

Highlight the Sun's actions.

Underline the words that show what the Sun made the man do. This will help you find the answer to question 1.

Now it was the Sun's turn. She came out from behind the cloud and shone brightly. The man began to sweat from the heat and decided he could go no further. So he stopped, took off his coat, and continued his walk.

Put a box around a sentence that shows what effect the Sun had on the man.

1 What is the **main idea** of the text?

_____

_____

_____

2 Which **three details** helped you find the main idea?

a _____

_____

_____

b _____

_____

_____

c _____

_____

_____

RL.3.2 Recount stories, including fables, folktales, and myths from diverse cultures; determine the central message, lesson, or moral and explain how it is conveyed through key details in the text.

Suffix: ing

> The suffix **ing** is added to a verb to show something is still happening. When the base form of the verb ends in a consonant with a <u>short vowel before</u> it, **double the consonant** before adding **ing**; e.g., r<u>u</u>n → ru**nn**ing, ch<u>a</u>t → cha**tt**ing.

List **1** **Write the word.**

batting _____

fitting _____

hopping _____

getting _____

winning _____

rotting _____

running _____

tapping _____

fanning _____

sitting _____

clapping _____

shutting _____

dropping _____

slipping _____

dripping _____

shopping _____

chatting _____

tripping _____

grabbing _____

swimming _____

2 **Unscramble these list words.**

a ttbaing _____

b ppingtri _____

c bbgraing _____

d sliingpp _____

e ingfitt _____

f nnniigw _____

3 **Opposites.** Find the opposite.

a losing _____

b opening _____

c standing _____

d giving _____

e walking _____

4 **Missing letters.** Write the missing letters.

a ___op ___ ___ ___ ___ ___

b r___ ___ ___ni ___g

c ___rop ___ ___ ___ ___ ___g

d ch ___ ___ ___tin ___

e dri ___ ___ ___i ___g

5 **Underline the mistakes.** Write the word correctly.

a The children are runing around the oval. _____

b The sound of the driping faucet kept me up all night. _____

c I was startled when I heard someone tappping on the window. _____

d I found the cat siting on the windowsill. _____

e People are always sliping over on the wet tiles. _____

f The apples are roting on the compost. _____

L.3.2.E Use conventional spelling for high-frequency and other studied words and for adding suffixes to base words.

59

Suffix: ing

1 **Revise your spelling list from page 60.** Complete each sentence with a list word.

a The children are _____ in their new pool.

b She is _____ a new kitten.

c It's so hot, I am _____ myself with a newspaper.

d The apple was so old it was _____ .

e We could hear the crowd _____ and cheering.

f At 3 goals to 2, ours was the _____ team.

g We are _____ for some new winter clothes.

h She keeps _____ over her own feet.

Challenge words

2 **Write the word.**

splitting _____

wrapping _____

scrapping _____

beginning _____

programming _____

permitting _____

forbidding _____

submitting _____

squatting _____

regretting _____

3 **Hidden words.** Find the challenge word.

a bifoforbiddingfid _____

b bitsubmittingus _____

c uqtsisquattingisu _____

d crpscrappingcrp _____

e rawrappingwrpi _____

4 **Complete the sentence.**

a He is _____ wood for the fire.

b My brother is _____ our computer to fight viruses.

c She is _____ not bringing her sweater on such a cold day.

d Next week, we're going camping, weather _____ .

L.3.2.E Use conventional spelling for high-frequency and other studied words and for adding suffixes to base words.

Auxiliary verbs

Auxiliary (helping) verbs are verbs that help other verbs do their work. They come before the main verb; e.g., I **am** jumping.

1 **Complete each sentence with a helping verb from the box.**

a I _____ heard the news.

b We _____ going to the circus.

c He _____ not know who I am.

d I _____ doing my homework.

e It _____ raining when we left.

f She _____ finished her work.

g He _____ brushing his teeth.

am	is	are
was	has	
have	does	

2 **Color the incorrect verb. Write it correctly.**

a My mother are speaking to my coach. _____

b I has just seen my friend drive past. _____

c I are drinking a glass of milk. _____

d Maya do not hear what I said. _____

e Adam have left his book at home. _____

f The bees was buzzing about the hive. _____

g The children does not know their geography. _____

3 **Choose the right verb.**

a I (have/has) eaten five servings of fruit and vegetables today.

b We (is/are) going to Egypt to see the pyramids.

c My aunt and uncle (is/are) coming for Thanksgiving.

d (Is/Are) you coming to my party?

e My friends (was/were) waiting for me at the bus stop.

f Jordan (was/were) riding her skateboard in the driveway.

Invisi-pets

Making inferences
To make inferences while reading, use clues in the text. The clues help you find the answers that are hiding in the text.

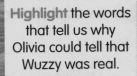

Read the passage.

Circle the words that tell us what color Wuzzy was.

Underline the sentence that gives the best description of Wuzzy.

Highlight the words that tell us why Olivia could tell that Wuzzy was real.

"What's a Whoowuzzler?" asked Olivia.

"It's an invisible pet," said Sam. "I've called mine Wuzzy."

"And what exactly does Wuzzy look like?" asked Olivia, putting her hand in the box. It was a shock to find that she could feel something small and soft even though she couldn't see anything.

"Well, he kind of looks like a guinea pig but he has feathers instead of fur. His feathers are red, with a few blue ones on his belly," Sam replied.

Olivia slowly felt the creature in the box all over. She had to agree that it was exactly what Wuzzy felt like—a feather-covered guinea pig.

Circle the correct answer for each question.

1 What can we **infer** about Wuzzy from Sam's description?
- a Wuzzy is furry.
- b Wuzzy is colorful.
- c Wuzzy is tiny.
- d Wuzzy is scruffy.

2 Which words are **clues** to question 1's answer?
- a *guinea pig*
- b *kind* and *looks*
- c *feathers* and *fur*
- d *red* and *blue*

3 What other **inference** can we make about Wuzzy? Wuzzy is …
- a a guinea pig.
- b a bird.
- c an unusual creature.
- d a soft toy.

4 Which phrase is the **clue** to question 3's answer?
- a a feather-covered guinea pig
- b creature in the box
- c looks like a guinea pig
- d a shock

RL.3.1 Ask and answer questions to demonstrate understanding of a text, referring explicitly to the text as the basis for the answers.

Invisi-pets

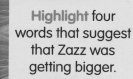

Read the whole story

Read the passage.

<u>Underline</u> how Zazz moved.

(Circle) words that tell you that Wuzzy and Zazz were noisy.

Back at home, Zazz grew as fast as Wuzzy had done, but not from eating. The more she bounced the more Zazz grew. And she bounced everywhere! Wuzzy's screeching was no longer the problem. Now it was the thumping of Zazz's long tail.

The only way to stop the thumping was to get Zazz to jump on the bed. When Wuzzy saw how much fun jumping on the bed was, he wanted to do it too. And, when Olivia and Sam saw how much fun their invisi-pets were having bouncing on the bed, they couldn't help but join in.

Highlight four words that suggest that Zazz was getting bigger.

Put a boxed around the word that names a part of Zazz's body.

1. We can **infer** that Zazz has lots of energy. What is the **clue**?

_____

2. Which two words **suggest** that Wuzzy and Zazz are noisy creatures?

_____

3. Write a description of Zazz based on **clues** in the text.

_____

_____

4. What does the word *invisi-pets* **suggest** about Wuzzy and Zazz?

_____

5. **How can we tell** that Olivia and Sam enjoy playing with their pets?

_____

RL.3.1 Ask and answer questions to demonstrate understanding of a text, referring explicitly to the text as the basis for the answers.

63

ei, ey, eigh

A **digraph** is two letters that make a single sound. Sometimes the letters **ei** make the single sound **ay**; e.g., r**ei**n. Sometimes the letters **ey** make the single sound **ay**; e.g., ob**ey**. The letters **eigh** usually make the sound **ay**; e.g., n**eigh**.

List

reins
prey
vein
veil
eight
whey
they
obey
weigh
neigh
weighed
beige
eighth
sleigh
obeyed
obeying
weighing
eighty
eighteen
eighteenth

1 Write the word.

_____
_____
_____
_____
_____
_____
_____
_____
_____
_____
_____
_____
_____
_____
_____
_____
_____
_____
_____
_____

2 Sort the words.

ei	ey	eigh
_____	_____	_____
_____	_____	_____
_____	_____	_____
_____	_____	_____
_____	_____	_____
_____	_____	_____
_____	_____	_____
		_____
		_____
		_____

3 Word clues. Which list word means?

a   one more than seventy-nine _____

b   Miss Muffet ate her curds and _____

c   two less than twenty _____

d   the sound a horse makes _____

e   worn over the face _____

f   one more than seven _____

g   following a command _____

4 Meaning. Which list word means?

a   Leather straps attached to a horse's bridle _____

b   An animal that is hunted by another _____

c   To measure using a scale _____

d   A cart used to transport people over snow _____

e   Vessel that carries blood to the heart _____

f   To carry out a command or instructions _____

L.3.2.F Use spelling patterns and generalizations in writing words.

ei, ey, eigh

1 **Revise your spelling list from page 64.** Underline the mistake. Write the word correctly.

a   One less than nineteen is eyteen.   _____

b   Her pants were a boring beighe color.   _____

c   We are weying things in the kitchen to find the heaviest item.   _____

d   I've already read seven of her books; I'm now on the eyghth.   _____

e   The rules of the game must be obeighed.   _____

f   My grandfather is eity years old.   _____

Challenge words

2 **Write the word.**

convey   _____

survey   _____

neighing   _____

freighter   _____

neighbor   _____

feint   _____

neighborly   _____

freight   _____

lightweight   _____

weightlifter   _____

3 **Word clues.** Which challenge word means?

a   to collect specific information

_____

b   a ship that transports goods

_____

c   a person that lives close to you

_____

d   a false movement

_____

e   a noise a horse makes

_____

4 **Complete the sentence.**

a   The horses were _____ loudly.

b   I will _____ the news to them.

c   I wasn't fooled by his _____ to the right.

d   Most _____ travels by air.

e   We tallied the _____ data.

f   A feather is considered to be very _____.

Future tense

The **future tense** is formed by placing the auxiliary verb **will** before the **main verb**; e.g., I **will eat** later. It can also be formed by using the auxiliary verbs **am**, **is**, or **are** with **going to**; e.g., They **are going to** meet us at the theater.

1 **Complete each sentence with a verb from the box.**

a That man will _____ you a ticket.

b She is going to _____ the water.

c The children will _____ their bicycles.

d I am going to _____ you a cup of tea.

e They are going to _____ a new house.

f Our parents will _____ us play baseball.

g Tony is going to _____ with his puppy.

make boil play ride
give build watch

2 **Complete each sentence by filling in the missing word.**

a You _____ miss your bus if you don't hurry.

b My mother _____ going to fetch me later.

c I _____ going to visit my cousins tomorrow.

d Claire _____ going to meet us at the park.

e Alex is _____ to invite me to his party.

f The children are going _____ clean their rooms.

3 **Write endings for the following sentences.**

a Sophia is going to _____

_____

b I am going to _____

_____

c The children are going to _____

_____

L.3.1.E Form and use the simple verb tenses.

Toothless!

Sequencing events
To identify the sequence of events in a text, look at numbers and words that give clues to the order in which things happen.

Read the passage.

Underline the first thing Lucy did.

Color the words that show what Lucy said **while** Crazy Cleaner was chugging through the surf.

Underline the question Granddad asked **when** he saw steam coming out of Crazy Cleaner.

Highlight the words that tell us what Lucy did **before** she turned Crazy Cleaner on.

Circle the words that show that Crazy Cleaner threw the umbrella after the hat.

Granddad and Lucy wheeled *Crazy Cleaner* down to the beach. Lucy set its dials to 'underwater' and 'pickup'. She pushed it into the water and turned it on. *Crazy Cleaner* chugged through the surf.

"Now we'll find your teeth," said Lucy.

"Is it supposed to spurt out steam like that?" asked Granddad. Steam was pouring from *Crazy Cleaner's* engine.

"Oh no! Something's wrong," said Lucy. "Look! It's heading up the beach." *Crazy Cleaner* was chugging over the sand towards them.

"Watch out!" shouted Granddad. They ducked, as *Crazy Cleaner* threw a hat at them and then an umbrella.

1 **Number the sentences from 1–7 to show the order in which the events happened.**

☐ Steam started coming out of *Crazy Cleaner's* engine.

☐ Lucy set the dials on *Crazy Cleaner*.

☐ Lucy said that something was wrong with *Crazy Cleaner*.

☐ *Crazy Cleaner* threw an umbrella at Granddad and Lucy.

☐ Granddad and Lucy pushed *Crazy Cleaner* down to the beach.

☐ *Crazy Cleaner* chugged through the surf.

☐ *Crazy Cleaner* threw a hat at Granddad and Lucy.

RL.3.1 Ask and answer questions to demonstrate understanding of a text, referring explicitly to the text as the basis for the answers.

67

Toothless!

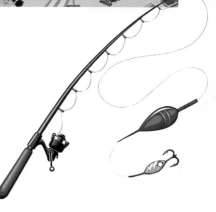

Read the whole story

Read the passage.

Highlight
Lucy's first action.

Color what Granddad did **after** he grabbed his fishing rod.

"Are we there yet? Is this the spot?" asked Granddad, staring into the water.

Lucy pulled a map out of her pocket and studied it. "Yes, this is it."

Granddad grabbed his fishing rod. He put a prawn on his hook. Lucy grabbed her fishing rod. Then, she pulled a metal box from her pocket. She tied it to the end of her fishing line.

"Isn't that *Doggie's Little Helper*?" asked Granddad. "How's that going to find my teeth?"

"It used to be *Doggie's Little Helper*, but I've fixed it. Now it finds false teeth instead of dog bones," said Lucy.

<u>Underline</u> what Lucy said **while** she studied the map.

Put a box around what Lucy did **before** she pulled the metal box from her pocket.

1 **Write the following events in the correct sequence.**

- Meanwhile Granddad put a prawn on his hook.
- Granddad asked if it was *Doggie's Little Helper*.
- Then Lucy pulled a metal box out of her pocket.
- First, Lucy pulled a map out of her pocket and studied it.
- Lucy said she'd fixed it and now it found false teeth.
- She tied the box to the end of her fishing line.

_____

_____

_____

_____

_____

RL.3.1 Ask and answer questions to demonstrate understanding of a text, referring explicitly to the text as the basis for the answers.

Endings: le, el, al

Most two-syllable words that end in the **l** sound have the letters **le** at the end; e.g., pur**ple**.

Some two-syllable words that end in the **l** sound have the letters **el** at the end; e.g., trav**el** and some have **al**; e.g., roy**al**.

List ① **Write the word.**

little _____

table _____

uncle _____

angel _____

apple _____

royal _____

candle _____

bottle _____

camel _____

final _____

purple _____

temple _____

gentle _____

normal _____

cattle _____

bundle _____

travel _____

local _____

people _____

equal _____

② **Sort the words.**

le	el	al
_____	_____	_____
_____	_____	_____
_____	_____	_____
_____	_____	_____
_____	_____	_____
_____	_____	_____
_____	_____	_____
_____	_____	_____
_____	_____	_____
_____	_____	_____
_____	_____	_____

③ **In a group.** Write the list word that belongs in each group.

a tiny, small, _____

b king, queen, _____

c pear, orange, _____

d journey, vacation, _____

e sheep, horses, _____

f aunty, cousin, _____

④ **Name.**

a _____ b _____ c _____ d _____

Endings: le, el, al

1 **Revise your spelling list from page 69.** Which list word means?

a To have the same value or amount as something else _____

b A place of worship _____

c A stick of wax burned to give light _____

d Large animal used for crossing deserts _____

e A piece of furniture with a flat top _____

f Used to hold liquid _____

g Your dad's brother _____

Challenge words

2 **Write the word.**

marvel _____

parcel _____

example _____

floral _____

trouble _____

couple _____

channel _____

tribal _____

struggle _____

vehicle _____

3 **Complete the sentence.**

a I received a _____ in the mail.

b A daffodil is an _____ of a flower.

c My brother got into _____ for breaking Mom's vase.

d I wanted to change the _____ but couldn't find the remote!

e It was a _____ to get my new bed upstairs.

f A car is an example of a _____.

g She has a _____ pattern on her shorts.

4 **Word clues.** Which challenge word means?

a flower pattern _____

b transport _____

c hard _____

d wonder _____

e model to be copied _____

L.3.2.F Use spelling patterns and generalizations in writing words.

Progressive tense

The **progressive tense** describes an action that is, was, or will be happening. It has an **auxiliary verb before** the **main verb**; e.g., She **is skipping**. He **was working**. They **will be running**.

1 **Fill in the verbs.**

| were sitting | are planning | is coloring | will be cheering | was standing |

a   She _____ in her picture.

b   He _____ on one leg.

c   You _____ on my chair.

d   We _____ a surprise party for his birthday.

e   Everyone _____ for their favorite team.

2 **Color the verb that is wrong. Correct the error.**

a   I is reading an interesting book.   _____

b   I were climbing the tree when I fell.   _____

c   She were showing them her new game.   _____

d   He is close the window because he is cold. _____

e   She will be leave for Europe in the morning. _____

f   They was meeting their friends at the movies. _____

3 **Complete the table.**

Present progressive	Past progressive	Future progressive
I am crying.		I will be crying.
She is driving.		
	They were fighting.	
You are selling.		
It is barking.		
	She was hiding.	
They are shouting.		

L.3.1.I Produce simple, compound, and complex sentences.

It's a Mystery

Compare and contrast
To compare and contrast information, look for the similarities and differences between details in the text.

Read the passage.

Highlight the CSIs' main job.

Underline the lab-based forensic scientists' main job.

Circle the names of the different types of medical forensic scientists.

Each member of the forensic team has his or her own job.

Crime scene investigators (or CSIs) examine the scene of the crime and collect evidence.

Lab-based forensic scientists carefully analyze this material, often using the latest technology.

Medical forensic scientists, such as pathologists and dentists, are called in if they are needed.

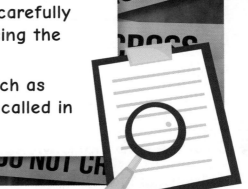

CRIME

Circle the correct answer for each question.

1 How are members of a forensic team **different**? They …

a work in different cities.
b wear different uniforms.
c do different jobs.
d speak different languages.

2 How are CSIs and lab-based forensic scientists **alike**? They both …

a examine the scene of the crime.
b try to solve a crime.
c analyze material using microscopes.
d work in a laboratory.

3 How are lab-based and medical forensic scientists **similar**?

a Neither uses technology.
b Both help CSIs collect evidence.
c Both work outdoors.
d Both analyze evidence.

4 How are lab-based and medical forensic scientists **different**? Medical forensic scientists are …

a not always needed.
b the first ones on the scene.
c always needed.
d the most important members of the team.

RI.3.8 Describe the logical connection between particular sentences and paragraphs in a text.

It's a Mystery

Read the full text

It's a Mystery

Read the passage.

Underline the similarity between archeologists and detectives.

Highlight the different things Ötzi might have used his cloak for.

Archeologists are like detectives. They look for clues too. But they're not looking for clues to a crime; they're looking for clues to the past. The archeologists called the iceman "Ötzi", and set out to investigate his mystery.

Ötzi was wearing his cloak when he died. It was braided from long grasses, and would have been a waterproof layer over his fur clothes. He probably also used it as a blanket or a ground cover.

Color the different kinds of clues archeologists and detectives look for.

Circle different materials Ötzi's clothes were made from.

1. How are archeologists and detectives **alike**?

_____

2. How are archeologists and detectives **different**?

_____

_____

3. What **different** things do archeologists think Ötzi used his cloak for?

_____

_____

4. What **different** materials were Ötzi's clothes made from?

_____

5. In the following sentence, circle the correct word.

Ötzi's cloak and clothes were both made from natural / synthetic materials.

Suffix: ed

When the suffix **ed** is added to a verb, it changes the verb from the present tense to the **past tense**. The past tense shows that something has already happened; e.g., kick**ed**. When a verb ends in **e**, just add **d**; e.g., smil**ed**.

List ① **Write the word.**

asked _____

cooked _____

mixed _____

yelled _____

dusted _____

cared _____

liked _____

tamed _____

hoped _____

loved _____

washed _____

kicked _____

roared _____

smiled _____

stared _____

pleased _____

spilled _____

warmed _____

roasted _____

poured _____

② **Unscramble the words.**

a ovdle _____

b mrawed _____

c staoedr _____

d dekcik _____

e heasdw _____

f usdted _____

g milsed _____

③ **Missing letter.** Write the missing letter.

a y ___ ___ led

b ___ oo ___ ___ ___

c pl ___ ___ ___ ed

d a ___ ___ ___ d

e ___ ___ ured

f r ___ ___ ___ ed

g m ___ ___ ___ d

h ___ ___ ill ___ ___

④ **Chunks.** Rearrange the chunks to make a list word.

a ed ar m w _____

b sh ed wa _____

c ed k k ic _____

d as ed le p _____

e ill ed sp _____

f as ted ro _____

⑤ **Complete the tables.**

Present tense	Past tense
smile	
	liked
dust	
yell	

Present tense	Past tense
	cooked
	washed
love	
mix	

L.3.1.E Form and use the simple verb tenses.

Suffix: ed

1 **Revise your spelling list from page 74.** Underline the spelling mistakes. Write the word correctly.

a   My piano teacher was plesed I had practiced my new piece. _____

b   The circus performer taimed the wild lion. _____

c   We rosted marshmallows around the campfire. _____

d   The heater warmd our freezing hands and feet. _____

e   Mom got angry when I spillid hot chocolate on the carpet. _____

f   Dad cooced so much spaghetti that we still have leftovers. _____

g   I kiked the ball so high that it landed on the roof! _____

Challenge words

2 **Write the word.**

enjoyed   _____

praised   _____

visited   _____

wheeled   _____

ordered   _____

admired   _____

appeared   _____

breathed   _____

frightened   _____

remembered   _____

3 **Complete the sentence.**

a   Sam e_____ his visit to the zoo.

b   I v_____ my grandparents.

c   Mom o_____ pizza for dinner.

d   I r_____ to return my overdue library books.

e   Dad p_____ us for our good behavior.

f   I a_____ him for his bravery.

g   He a_____ out of nowhere.

h   I w_____ the shopping cart down the supermarket aisles.

4 **Hidden words.** Find the challenge word hidden in these letters.

a   earpeappearedere _____

b   arisepraisedprai _____

c   eatbrbreathedklp _____

d   rredoordereddde _____

e   ghtefrfrightenedefri _____

f   emremembereded _____

g   welwheeledhwehel _____

h   mireadmiredded _____

i   joyenjoyedenjo _____

j   ttdevisitedvssit _____

Commas in lists

A **comma** (,) shows a pause in a sentence. It separates words in lists; e.g., I like apples, peaches, and pears.

1 **Fill in the commas in these lists.**

 a bread eggs milk and cheese

 b cows goats sheep and pigs

 c two four six or eight

 d shirts shorts hats and shoes

 e cars vans buses or trains

 f cups saucers plates and bowls

2 **Write these items as a list.**

_____

_____

_____

3 **Fill in the commas in these sentences.**

 a There were forks spoons and knives in the picnic basket.

 b December January and February are the coldest months of the year.

 c Yellow orange and green are my favorite colors.

 d I packed sandwiches apples candy and a bottle of water in my knapsack for the bus ride to Grandma's house.

 e I saw lizards spiders and snakes at the zoo.

 f Did you want to go the movies the park or the mall?

 g I've been to Beijing Hong Kong and Tokyo.

 h Dad bought eggs bread and milk at the market.

 i We have a pet rabbit two fish and a very spoilt cat.

 j Would you like lasagne sushi or burgers for dinner?

 k My beach bag contains a towel sunscreen and a book to read.

L.3.2 Demonstrate command of the conventions of standard English capitalization, punctuation, and spelling when writing.

TV Guide

Read the passage.

Point of view
To identify point of view, look at the way characters act or feel. In reviews, the writer's point of view can be seen in their word choices. Phrases like "I believe" or "we think" tell the reader the information is the writer's opinion.

Color the event that made Darren change his mind about his party.

It's Darren's birthday, and he's looking forward to his party until he discovers Mother's bunny decorations! He asks Kerry the goldfish for help, but Admiral Bubbles-in-a-Bowl has other ideas.

Darren Eller Dressed in Yella helps children see foreign lands—in their own rooms. With a new, crazy adventure each week, kids discover that there are magical worlds, full of funny characters, right in their own homes.

Circle two adjectives that help to show the reviewer's opinion of the program.

Circle the correct answer for each question.

1 How does Darren **feel** about his birthday party before he sees the bunny decorations?

  a He is nervous about it.   b He is angry about it.

  c He is looking forward to it.   d He does not want a party.

2 When do Darren's **feelings** about his party start to change?

  a when he sees his mother   b when he speaks to Kerry the goldfish

  c when Admiral Bubbles-in-a-Bowl arrives   d when he sees the bunny decorations

3 Which punctuation helps us to understand Darren's **feelings** about the bunny decorations?

  a .   b ,   c !   d '

4 In the second paragraph, the reviewer calls the show *funny*. This tells us the reviewer thinks the program is ...

  a boring.   b entertaining.   c exciting.   d scary.

TV Guide

Read the passage.

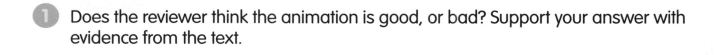

Underline what the reviewer thinks of the animation.

Highlight the things children can learn from the program.

The animation in this show is always bright, on the go, and very detailed. It doesn't have the homemade look that is popular in children's television these days. As children follow Darren's adventures, they explore everyday emotions, such as love, fear, and happiness, and see how Darren and his family respond to challenges. Highly recommended.

Put a box around the reviewer's overall opinion of the program.

1 Does the reviewer think the animation is good, or bad? Support your answer with evidence from the text.

_____

_____

_____

2 Does the reviewer believe that children can learn something from the program? Support your answer with evidence from the text.

_____

_____

_____

3 Would you recommend this program to someone with a young child? Why, or why not?

_____

_____

_____

RI.3.1 Ask and answer questions to demonstrate understanding of a text, referring explicitly to the text as the basis for the answers.

Homophones

> **Homophones** are words that sound the same but are spelled differently and have different meanings; e.g., peace, piece.

List ① **Write the word.**

mane _____

main _____

meat _____

meet _____

plane _____

plain _____

for _____

four _____

by _____

buy _____

not _____

knot _____

seen _____

scene _____

great _____

grate _____

groan _____

grown _____

who's _____

whose _____

② **In a group.** Write the list word that belongs in each group.

a tail, claw, _____

b car, boat, _____

c moan, cry, _____

d fantastic, wonderful, _____

e two, three, _____

f rope, string, _____

g bought, purchase, _____

③ **Word clues.** Which list word means?

a no decoration _____

b very good _____

c the most important _____

d the number after three _____

e place an event happens _____

f food cooked on a barbecue _____

g a grunt or deep sound _____

h next to or near _____

i to have looked at _____

j who is _____

④ **Name.**

a _____ b _____ c _____ d _____

Homophones

1 **Revise your spelling list from page 79.** Underline the spelling mistake. Write the word correctly.

a   The lion had a big bushy main.   _____

b   Who's backpack is at the door?   _____

c   The recipe says to great two whole carrots.   _____

d   I didn't have money to by an ice cream.   _____

e   My younger sister is for years old.   _____

f   Have you scene the remote?   _____

g   We agreed to meat after soccer practice.   _____

Challenge words

2   **Write the word.**

herd   _____

heard   _____

berry   _____

bury   _____

heel   _____

heal   _____

he'll   _____

rain   _____

rein   _____

reign   _____

3 **Word clues.** Which challenge word means?

a   group of animals   _____

b   a small juicy fruit   _____

c   water from the sky   _____

d   leather strap   _____

e   part of your foot   _____

f   make healthy again   _____

4 **Complete the sentence.**

a   I _____ a loud noise and went to investigate.

b   The weather forecast predicted heavy _____.

c   The dog likes to _____ bones in the backyard.

d   The _____ of cows grazed quietly in the paddock.

L.3.2.F Use spelling patterns and generalizations in writing words.

Plural nouns

A **plural noun** names more than one person, thing, or place. Most plural nouns are formed by adding **s** or **es** to the singular; e.g., wall**s**, bush**es**. Sometimes other letters have to change before adding **s** or **es**; e.g., diar**y** → diar**ies**, lea**f** → lea**ves**. Sometimes plural nouns are formed in other ways; e.g., child → child**ren**.

1 **Color the noun that correctly completes each sentence.**

a The man found three (fly, flies) in his soup.

b The children put their (hat, hats) on their heads.

c I saw several large gray (elephant, elephants) in the distance.

d My mother bought two (loaf, loaves) of bread at the bakery.

e I added a handful of (berry, berries) to my granola.

f Two (man, men) carried the heavy box inside.

g The carpenter made two (notch, notches) in the wood.

2 **Complete the table.**

One	Two	One	Two
ant	*ants*	potato	
brush		half	
rabbit		wash	
knife		tiger	
match		woman	

3 **In each sentence, write the noun in parentheses correctly.**

a The (girl) _____ ate their lunch outside.

b The dog has two white (patch) _____ on its head.

c I bought a box of (cherry) _____ at the market.

d Everyone says a cat has nine (life) _____.

e I sliced two (tomato) _____ to add to the salad.

L.3.1.B Form and use regular and irregular plural nouns.

81

Posters

Study the poster.

Circle the words that tell when the event is.

Put a box around where the event will be.

Highlight the list of legends.

Circle the correct answer for each question.

1 What is the best **conclusion**? Pick in the Park takes place in the ...
   a spring.   b fall.   c winter.   d summer.

2 Which word is the **clue** to question 1's answer?
   a Saturday   b February   c Park   d Pick

3 What is the best **conclusion**? The performance will take place ...
   a outdoors.   b on a boat.   c on a beach.   d in a hall.

4 Which word is the **clue** to question 3's answer?
   a legends   b Tickets   c Pick   d Park

5 What **conclusion** can we draw from the list of legends?
   a The concert will be over in minutes.   b The concert will run for a few hours.
   c The legends are mainly students.   d The legends are mainly teenagers.

RI.3.1 Ask and answer questions to demonstrate understanding of a text, referring explicitly to the text as the basis for the answers.

Posters

1 Which **five conclusions** can we draw from the words and pictures in the poster? Circle the correct answers.

a   Green aliens like to read.

b   There are books on many different topics.

c   Aliens sometimes read scary books.

d   Reading can be exciting.

e   Aliens are wild creatures.

f   People who read are wild.

g   Some books are about unusual things.

h   Libraries have a wide variety of books.

i   Aliens scream when they are scared.

j   There are libraries in most neighborhoods.

RI.3.1 Ask and answer questions to demonstrate understanding of a text, referring explicitly to the text as the basis for the answers.

83

Silent k, g, w

A **digraph** is two letters that make a single sound. The digraphs **kn** and **gn** make the single sound **n**; e.g., **kn**ot, **gn**ome. The digraph **wr** makes the single sound **r**; e.g., **wr**ite, **wr**ap. The letters **g** and **w** are sometimes silent elsewhere in a word; e.g., forei**g**n, ans**w**er.

List **1** **Write the word.**

knee _____
knit _____
knot _____
know _____
sign _____
knight _____
reign _____
sword _____
write _____
knock _____
knife _____
knead _____
knack _____
gnat _____
wren _____
design _____
gnome _____
gnash _____
wreck _____
wrong _____

2 **Sort the words.**

silent *k*	silent *g*	silent *w*
_____	_____	_____
_____	_____	_____
_____	_____	_____
_____	_____	_____
_____	_____	_____
_____	_____	_____
_____	_____	_____
_____	_____	_____
_____	_____	_____

3 **Name.**

a _____

b _____

c _____

d _____

4 **Word clues.** Which list word means?

a a weapon with a long pointed blade _____
b a small fairy tale creature _____
c the joint in a leg _____
d a small insect with two wings _____
e a king or queen's time of ruling _____
f a small brown bird

L.3.2.F Use spelling patterns and generalizations in writing words.

Silent k, g, w

1 **Revise your spelling list from page 84.** Underline the spelling mistake. Write the word correctly.

a My sisters and I like to desin new forms of transport. _____

b We dived down to the old reck. _____

c I eat dinner with a nife and fork. _____

d You must nead the dough before baking it in the oven. _____

e I rite in my journal every night. _____

f I couldn't see the street sin, so we missed the turn-off. _____

g My mom is teaching me how to nit my own scarf. _____

Challenge words

2 **Write the word.**

knuckle _____

knapsack _____

gnarl _____

wrestle _____

knowledge _____

written _____

foreign _____

wrought _____

wreckage _____

playwright _____

3 **Word clues.** Which challenge word means?

a a knot or bulge _____

b one who writes plays _____

c the joint in a finger _____

d a bag _____

e to struggle or fight _____

f from another country _____

4 **Complete the sentence.**

a Mia couldn't get the ring over her _____.

b I packed my library books into my _____.

c College professors have a lot of _____.

d She had _____ an excellent story.

e The _____ was in the ocean.

L.3.2.F Use spelling patterns and generalizations in writing words.

85

Possessive pronouns

A possessive pronoun **stands in place of a noun**. It shows **ownership or possession**; e.g., my, his, their.

1 **Complete each sentence with a pronoun from the box.** Use each pronoun once.

a Is this scarf _____?

b He gave it to me, so now it is _____.

c The farmers all have _____ own tractors.

d The girl showed us _____ new violin.

e _____ dog wags _____ tail when it sees us.

f Why are you sitting in _____ room?

g The artist sold _____ paintings to a gallery.

> mine   his   our
> yours   her   your
> their   its

2 **Complete the sentences.** If something belongs to...

me, it is _mine_ .

b him, it is _____ .

d them, it is _____ .

a you, it is _____ .

c her, it is _____ .

e us, it is _____ .

3 **Sort the words.**

One owner		More than one owner
_____	mine our	_____
_____	ours their	_____
_____	his hers	_____
_____	its theirs	_____

4 **Which word correctly completes the sentence?**

a Manuel gave the dog (it's, its) _____ dinner.

b Ollie says that blue car is (your, yours) _____ .

c Jodie left (her, hers) _____ watch in the bathroom.

d The house with the bright red door is (our, ours) _____ .

L.3.1.A Explain the function of pronouns in general and their functions in particular sentences.

Forests

Read the passage.

Finding the main idea and supporting details
To discover what a text is about, look for the main idea or key point. Facts and details in the text help you find the main idea.

Circle all the names of animals.

Highlight two kinds of forest.

Underline the number of animal species that inhabit a square mile in a rainforest.

Put a box around where possums are commonly found.

Forests are full of animals.

There are more insects in a forest than any other type of animal. They make up half the mass of all animal life in a rainforest.

About half of all the world's animal species live in tropical rainforests. Hundreds of bird, mammal, and reptile species live in each square mile of tropical rainforest.

Most rainforest mammals and reptiles are arboreal. This means they spend most of their lives in trees.

Small animals, such as possums, are common in temperate forests.

Circle the correct answer for each question.

1 What is the passage mainly about?
   a tropical and temperate forests
   b different kinds of insects
   c what forest animals look like
   d different kinds of forest animals

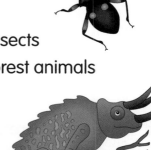

2 Which sentence best **supports** the main idea?
   a Most rainforest mammals and reptiles are arboreal.
   b Forests are full of animals.
   c This means they spend most of their lives in trees.
   d They make up half of all animal life in a rainforest.

3 Which word or phrase best **supports** the main idea?
   a mass
   b insects
   c live in trees
   d each square mile
   e bird, mammal, and reptile species
   f common

RI.3.2 Determine the main idea of a text; recount the key details and explain how they support the main idea.

87

Forests

Read the full text

Forests

Read the passage.

In paragraph 1, circle three words that can help us identify the main idea of the text.

Underline the words that tell us what people in forests use plants for.

Forest plants contain chemicals that can be made into medicines.

Plants make these chemicals to protect themselves from diseases, pests, and plant eaters.

People living in forests make medicines from plants. They use seeds, leaves, fruits, and bark.

Scientists also make medicines from forest plants. The medicines are used to treat asthma, cancer, and many other diseases. The drug Taxol, which is used to treat cancer, comes from the bark of the Pacific yew tree.

Highlight the diseases that medicines from forest plants are used to treat.

Put a box around the name of a specific drug that comes from a forest plant.

1 What is the **main idea** or **key point** of the text?

_____

_____

_____

2 Write down **three details** that support the main idea.

a _____

_____

b _____

_____

c _____

_____

RI.3.2 Determine the main idea of a text; recount the key details and explain how they support the main idea.

Suffixes: er, or

Adding the suffix **er** to a verb turns it into a noun; e.g., sing**er**. If the verb ends in **e**, just add **r**; e.g., danc**er**. If the verb ends in a consonant that has a **short vowel before it**, double the consonant before adding **er**; e.g., ru**nn**er.

Some verbs become nouns by adding the suffix **or**; e.g., edit**or**. If the verb **ends in e**, drop the **e** before adding **or**; e.g., decorat**e** → decorat**or**.

List **①** **Write the word.**

teacher _____

worker _____

seller _____

singer _____

swimmer _____

runner _____

driver _____

baker _____

collector _____

jogger _____

painter _____

gardener _____

climber _____

printer _____

editor _____

wrapper _____

director _____

conductor _____

supporter _____

builder _____

② **Sort the words.**

er	or
_____	_____
_____	_____
_____	_____
_____	_____
_____	_____
_____	_____
_____	_____
_____	_____
_____	_____
_____	_____
_____	_____
_____	_____
_____	_____
_____	_____

④ **Chunks.** Rearrange the syllables to make a list word.

a tor lec col _____

b duc tor con _____

c por sup ter _____

d ber clim _____

e ain p ter _____

③ **In a group.** Write the list word that belongs in each group.

a school, classroom, _____

b microphone, music, _____

c brushes, canvas, _____

d flour, bread, _____

e tools, bricks, _____

f pool, laps, _____

g plants, seeds, _____

Suffixes: er, or

1 **Revise your spelling list from page 89.** Underline the spelling mistakes.
Write the word correctly.

a The directer won an award for his latest film. _____

b I bought the book because it was a best sellor. _____

c My dad is a collecter of toy cars and old coins. _____

d The runnor was training hard for the marathon. _____

e His dream is to become the conducter of the
   New York Philharmonic Orchestra. _____

f The truck drivor has to be careful of smaller cars
   and vehicles on the road. _____

Challenge words

2 **Write the word.**

commander _____

manager _____

educator _____

attacker _____

knitter _____

decorator _____

elevator _____

exhibitor _____

navigator _____

foreigner _____

3 **Complete the sentence.**

a The professor is an _____.

b The store _____ gave us
   a discount.

c The _____ directed the ship.

d The _____ painted the
   room blue.

e The _____ made the longest
   scarf.

f The _____ felt nervous in the
   new country.

g We took the _____ to the
   top floor.

4 **Hidden words.** Find the challenge word hidden in these letters.

a ckerattackerattkl _____

b torceducatorduee _____

c recommanderand _____

d atorlelevatorele _____

e iborexhibitorexhiv _____

f ratordecoratorced _____

g angermanagere _____

h rkktknitterqlps _____

L.3.2.E Use conventional spelling for high-frequency and other studied words and for adding suffixes to base words.

Writing addresses

When writing **addresses**, use **commas** to separate:
- the name of the street from the name of the town or city
- the name of the town or city from the name of the state

For example: 12 Aspen Street, Columbus, Ohio 43207

1 **Check (✔) the addresses that have written correctly.**

a ☐ 1001 Morgan Drive, Chicago Illinois, 60609

b ☐ 1001 Morgan Drive, Chicago, Illinois 60609

c ☐ 1326 Sunland Boulevard, Los Angeles, California 900021

d ☐ 1326, Sunland Boulevard, Los Angeles, California, 900021

e ☐ 61046 Acorn Wood Way, Houston, Texas, 77014

f ☐ 61046 Acorn Wood Way, Houston, Texas 77014

2 **Fill in the commas in the following addresses.**

a 36 Woodbrook Terrace Springfield Massachusetts 01115

b 95 Alderwood Road Cleveland Ohio 44130

c 794 22nd Avenue Olympia Washington 98501

d 6 Maxwell Place Denver Colorado 80222

e 628 Alabama River Parkway Montgomery Alabama 36110

3 **Use the following information to write Tom's address.**

Tom lives in the state of Georgia. He lives in its oldest city, Savannah. His house number is 84. It is on Beechwood Drive. The zip code for Tom's address is 31403.

Tom's address is:

_____

_____

Marsupials

Read the passage.

Underline the reasons bilbies have become a vulnerable species.

The Australian greater bilby is the largest species of bandicoot. Bilbies are a vulnerable species. Cattle, sheep, and rabbits eat the food they need. Foxes and feral cats prey on them.

To save the greater bilby from extinction, they are bred in captivity and then released back into the wild.

Highlight the reason the greater bilby is bred in captivity.

Circle the correct answer for each question.

1 What has **caused** bilbies to become a vulnerable species?
   a predators and lack of food   **b** diseases and fires
   c air and soil pollution   **d** climate change

2 What **effect** has farming had on the bilby population? It has caused ...
   a bilby numbers to increase.   **b** bilbies to become extinct.
   c bilby numbers to decrease.   **d** bilbies to leave their habitat.

3 **Why** are greater bilbies bred in captivity?
   a to keep them safe from foxes and feral cats
   b to make sure they have enough food
   c to try to domesticate them
   d to prevent them from becoming extinct

4 What is the **result** of breeding greater bilbies in capitivity?
   a They lose their fear of humans.   **b** Scientists can learn more about their habits.
   c They are saved from extinction.   **d** They become stronger.

RI.3.3 Describe the relationship between a series of historical events, scientific ideas or concepts, or steps in technical procedures in a text, using language that pertains to time, sequence, and cause/effect.

Marsupials

Read the passage.

Underline the reason many Tasmanian devils have died.

Highlight what happens to Tasmanian devils that have tumors on their mouths.

Color the reason healthy Tasmanian devils are taken to wildlife parks.

Since 1996, many Tasmanian devils have died from a horrible disease. Lumps grow around the devil's mouth that turn into tumors. These spread across the face and body. The tumors make it hard for the devils to eat. Many starve to death.

Scientists are working to save the Tasmanian devil from extinction. They take healthy devils to wildlife parks. These disease-free animals breed with other healthy Tasmanian devils. In the future, they may be released into the wild.

Circle two adjectives that describe the Tasmanian devils the scientists use in their breeding program.

1 What has **caused** many Tasmanian devils to die?

_____

_____

2 How do tumors on the mouth **affect** the Tasmanian devils?

_____

_____

3 **Why** are scientists making sure only healthy Tasmanian devils breed with each other?

_____

_____

_____

4 What are scientists hoping will happen as a **result** of their breeding program for Tasmanian devils?

_____

_____

_____

RI.3.3 Describe the relationship between a series of historical events, scientific ideas or concepts, or steps in technical procedures in a text, using language that pertains to time, sequence, and cause/effect.

93

Digraphs: wh, ph, gh

A **digraph** is two consonants that make a single sound.
The consonants **wh**, make the sound **w**; e.g., **wh**eel.
The consonants **ph**, make the sound **f**; e.g., **ph**one.
The consonants **gh**, make the sound **g**; e.g., **gh**erkin.

List ① **Write the word.**

why _____

what _____

when _____

phone _____

ghost _____

white _____

which _____

while _____

graph _____

photo _____

whip _____

whale _____

where _____

phase _____

gherkin _____

wheat _____

whisper _____

wheel _____

whimper _____

whirl _____

② **In a group.** Write the list word that matches.

a camera _____

b data _____

c scared _____

d call _____

e ocean _____

f flour _____

g pickle _____

h quiet _____

③ **Complete each sentence with a list word.**

a I heard the _____ ringing, so ran to answer it.

b A blue _____ is the largest animal on Earth.

c I always pick the _____ out of my burger.

d I took a _____ of my cat with mom's new camera.

e The back _____ on my new bike is flat.

f The _____ fluffy cloud looked like an elephant in the sky.

④ **Name.**

a _____   b _____   c _____   d _____

Digraphs: wh, ph, gh

1 **Revise your spelling list from page 94.** Sort the words.

wh		ph	gh

Challenge words

2 **Write the word.**

whiskers _____

whelp _____

pharaoh _____

physical _____

wharf _____

whether _____

wheeze _____

photograph _____

ghoul _____

ghastly _____

3 **Hidden words.** Find the challenge word.

a phyisphysicalciphy _____

b thewewhetherthe _____

c eewhewheezeeze _____

d asthyghastlyghats _____

e arfwhwharfarfhw _____

f gaphotographggh _____

g lpwwhelpelpy _____

h aroahpharaoharah _____

i oughghoulool _____

j lghawhiskersgrsp _____

4 **Word clues.** Which challenge word means?

a king of Egypt _____

b hairs near a cat's mouth _____

c where ships and boats dock _____

L.3.2.F Use spelling patterns and generalizations in writing words.

95

Week 18 Day 5 Grammar

Subject-verb agreement

The **subject** in a sentence is the person or thing that **does the action**. The **verb** is the **action**; e.g., The **boy** (subject) **kicks** (verb) the ball. The subject and the verb must agree with each other; e.g., The **boy** **kicks** the ball. The **boys** **kick** the ball.

1 **Color the verb that correctly completes the sentence.**

a   The leaf (fall, falls) to the ground.

b   The doors (creak, creaks) open.

c   The water (splash, splashes) on the floor.

d   Our journey (end, ends) at the next town.

e   The children (go, goes) to school every day.

f   That boy and girl (live, lives) next door.

g   The window (rattle, rattles) when the wind blows.

h   Thunder (rumble, rumbles) in the distance.

2 **Choose a verb from each pair to complete the sentences.**

run runs	pick picks	watch watches	ride rides
hang hangs	sparkle sparkles	work works	

a   She _____ flowers for her mother.

b   We _____ during practice.

c   He _____ the train into the city.

d   The children _____ together as a team.

e   The dewdrops _____ in the sunshine.

f   We _____ the same movies on TV.

g   Not all paintings _____ on the wall.

96

L.3.1.F Ensure subject-verb agreement.

Spelling

Use this review to test your knowledge. It has three parts—**Spelling, Grammar,** and **Comprehension**. If you're unsure of an answer, go back and read the rules and generalizations in the blue boxes.

You have learned about:

- trigraph: igh
- endings: le, el, al
- silent k, g, w
- suffix: ing
- suffix: ed
- suffixes: er, or
- ei, ey, eigh
- homophones
- digraphs: wh, ph, gh

1 **The spelling mistakes in these sentences have been <u>underlined</u>. Write the correct spelling.** 2 marks

a The clock struck <u>midnite</u>. _____

b Arghhhhh! What an almighty <u>freyt</u>! _____

c Sam was <u>regreting</u> watching that scary film. _____

d Dad <u>weyghed</u> the pears at the market. _____

2 **This sentence has one word that is incorrect. Write the correct spelling.** 1 mark

Humans have used cameals as transport for thousands of years. _____

3 **Which pair of words correctly complete this sentence?** 1 mark

Do _____ tie your shoelaces in a _____.

a not   knot   b knot   not   c nott   knot   d nott   not

4 **Write ei, ey, or eigh to correctly complete these words.** 2 marks

a _____t   b surv _____   c v_____l   d b_____ge

5 **Each sentence has one word that is incorrect. Write the correct spelling.** 2 marks

a "They say this was King Arthur's sord," explained the guide. _____

b "My favorite flower is the dahlia," said the gardenor. _____

c When I grow up, I want to work at The New Yorker as an editer. _____

d Gross! There's a gerkin in my burger! _____

6 **Circle the correct verb to complete each sentence.** 2 marks

a The Statue of Liberty was (design, designed, designing) by French sculptor Frédéric Auguste Bartholdi.

b On Thursday night, my brother (cook, cooked, cooking) a delicious apple pie.

Your score

[ ]

10

Grammar

You have learned about:

- past and present tense
- progressive tense
- possessive pronouns
- auxiliary verbs
- commas in lists
- writing addresses
- future tense
- plural nouns
- subject-verb agreement

1 **In each sentence, write the underlined word in the past tense.** 2 marks

a The children <u>run</u> toward the sea.　＿＿＿＿＿＿＿＿＿＿＿

b The tiger <u>stalks</u> its prey.　＿＿＿＿＿＿＿＿＿＿＿

c The dog <u>eats</u> its dinner.　＿＿＿＿＿＿＿＿＿＿＿

d The girl <u>hops</u> on one leg.　＿＿＿＿＿＿＿＿＿＿＿

2 **Complete each sentence with an auxiliary verb from the box.** 2 marks

a The children ＿＿＿＿＿＿＿ waiting for the bus.

b I ＿＿＿＿＿＿＿ writing a story.

c The boy ＿＿＿＿＿＿＿ walking to the park.

d Rosie ＿＿＿＿＿＿＿ finished her chores.

am	has
are	is

3 **In the following sentences, fill in the missing verbs.** 2 marks

a Simon ＿＿＿＿＿＿＿ going to visit his friend tomorrow.

b Andy ＿＿＿＿＿＿＿ feed the dog when he gets home.

c My parents ＿＿＿＿＿＿＿ going to buy tickets for the show.

d Grandma and Grandpa ＿＿＿＿＿＿＿ be here soon.

4 **Write each sentence in the progressive tense.** 2 marks

a The boy plays with his toy soldiers.

＿＿＿＿＿＿＿＿＿＿＿＿＿＿＿＿＿＿＿＿＿＿＿＿＿＿＿＿＿＿＿

＿＿＿＿＿＿＿＿＿＿＿＿＿＿＿＿＿＿＿＿＿＿＿＿＿＿＿＿＿＿＿

b The children drew pictures for the art exhibit.

＿＿＿＿＿＿＿＿＿＿＿＿＿＿＿＿＿＿＿＿＿＿＿＿＿＿＿＿＿＿＿

＿＿＿＿＿＿＿＿＿＿＿＿＿＿＿＿＿＿＿＿＿＿＿＿＿＿＿＿＿＿＿

Grammar

5 **Use the words on the bags to complete each sentence.** 2 marks

a At the market I bought _____

_____

b At the zoo I saw _____

_____

tomatoes
bread
milk
cheese

elephants
lions
hippos
giraffes

6 **Complete the following table.** 3 marks

One	Two	One	Two
baby		monkey	
child		potato	
wish		leaf	

7 **Circle the pronoun that correctly completes each sentence.** 2 marks

a Jack said he would lend me (he, his) bike.

b Lauren let me play with (she, her) puppy.

c The children were told to bring (their, they) hats.

d I found the kitten under (your, you) bed.

8 **Use the information below to write Ava and Aiden's address.** 3 marks

Ava and Aiden live in Montgomery. It is the capital city of Alabama. They live at 446 Amanda Lane. The zip code for their address is 36110.

_____

_____

9 **Circle the word that correctly completes each sentence.** 2 marks

a The (man, men) are fixing the road.

b The dog (is, are) digging a hole in the garden.

c My friend (has, have) a rabbit and a hamster.

d The (bus, buses) always come late.

Your score

20

The Great Wall of China

Read the passage and then use the comprehension skills you have learned to answer the questions.

Powerful families called dynasties ruled over ancient China. Each dynasty brought new leaders. The leaders helped the people in different ways. Emperor Qin Shi Huang of the Qin Dynasty (221—206 BC) wanted to keep his people safe.

The Qin Dynasty started to build a wall to keep invaders out. Construction began in 220 BC and took 1,726 years to complete. The Ming Dynasty finished it in 1506.

The Great Wall is 4,500 miles long. It is the longest structure ever built. It runs from east to west along the border between China and Mongolia. The Wall crosses steep mountain ranges and deep valleys.

The Great Wall was built entirely by hand. It is made mostly of earth, brick, wood, and stone. Thousands of people worked on The Wall. Many died from injury, disease, and starvation.

UNESCO made The Great Wall a World Heritage Site in 1987. It ensures The Wall will be preserved for the future and restored. Thousands of tourists visit every year to see this Chinese treasure.

1 Which dynasty started building The Great Wall? 1 mark   LITERAL

    a the Tang Dynasty   **b** the Ming Dynasty

    c the Shang Dynasty   **d** the Qin Dynasty

2 What is a *dynasty*? 1 mark   CRITICAL

    a way to keep people safe   **b** rulers from the same family

    c an emperor   **d** servants of the king

The Great Wall of China

3 Give a text clue to support your answer to question 2. 2 marks — CRITICAL

_____

_____

_____

4 How long did it take to complete The Great Wall? 1 mark — LITERAL

a more than 1,500 years   b more than 2,700 years

c more than 2,000 years   d less than 1,700 years

5 Which are the TWO most likely reasons it took so long to build The Wall? 1 mark — CRITICAL

a Tourists slowed down construction.   b It was built by hand.

c It was a complicated design.   d It was very long.

6 What is the most likely reason many people died while building The Wall? 1 mark CRITICAL

a The workers were very old.   b The work was hard and dangerous.

c The Wall was badly built.   d The workers received no payment.

7 Give a text clue to support your answer to question 6. 2 marks — CRITICAL

_____

_____

_____

8 Who is an _invader_? A person who ... 1 mark — VOCABULARY

a migrates to another country.   b is unable to work.

c attacks and enters a country.   d is sick and spreads disease.

Your
score

☐
10

Your Review 2 Scores

Spelling		Grammar		Comprehension		Total
☐	+	☐	+	☐	=	☐
10		20		10		40

Chocolate Chuckles

Interpreting character behavior, feelings, and motivation

To interpret a character's feelings and what causes them to act in a certain way, look for clues in the text. The clues are usually in the words and punctuation.

Read the passage.

Circle words that give us clues about how Mom felt.

Put a box around the phrase that tells us the narrator was relieved about something.

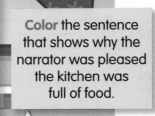

Color the sentence that shows why the narrator was pleased the kitchen was full of food.

"There's no milk!" said Mom as she slammed the fridge door closed. She turned around and glared at me.

I didn't say a word.

Luckily for me, the kitchen was full of cupcakes, cheese, cookies, bowls of chips, sausage rolls, pickled onions, streamers, hats, and blowers. In the middle of it all was a huge ginger birthday cake with "Happy 80th Birthday" around the edge.

Lucky for me because Mom couldn't see the empty milk carton I'd just been drinking from.

Circle the correct answer for each question.

1 When Mom says "There's no milk!", how does she most likely **sound**?

   a disappointed   b confused   c happy   d angry

2 Which **word** is a **clue** to question 1's answer?

   a turned   b glared   c fridge   d milk

3 Which **phrase** is a **clue** to question 1's answer?

   a slammed the fridge door   b turned around

   c Luckily for me   d a huge ginger birthday cake

4 Which **punctuation** is a **clue** to question 1's answer?

   a .   b ,   c !   d '

5 How would the narrator have **felt** when she realized her mom couldn't see the empty milk carton?

   a disappointed   b confused   c relieved   d afraid

RL.3.3 Describe characters in a story (e.g., their traits, motivations, or feelings) and explain how their actions contribute to the sequence of events.

Chocolate Chuckles

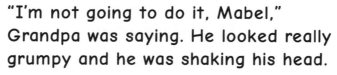
Read the whole story

Read the passage.

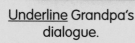
<u>Underline</u> Grandpa's dialogue.

Color the narrator's thoughts on Grandpa's teeth.

"I'm not going to do it, Mabel," Grandpa was saying. He looked really grumpy and he was shaking his head.

"My teeth are staying in my head until I die." He waggled them with his tongue. They were the most disgusting pair of falsies you've ever seen.

"They're so worn," said Grandma.

"It would be much easier to chew with new ones," said Mom.

In paragraph 1, **highlight** the words that show what Grandpa was doing.

Put a box around Grandma's dialogue.

 1 Which **word** tells us that Grandpa was in a **bad mood**?

_____

 2 **Why** was Grandpa in a bad mood?

_____

_____

 3 What was the **narrator's opinion** of Grandpa's false teeth?

_____

_____

 4 Why did **Grandma think** Grandpa needed new teeth?

_____

 5 Why did **Mom think** Grandpa should get new teeth?

_____

_____

RL.3.3 Describe characters in a story (e.g., their traits, motivations, or feelings) and explain how their actions contribute to the sequence of events.

Verb endings: ies, ied

Sometimes we have to add **s** or **es** to the base form of the verb to make it agree with its subject.

If the base form of the verb ends in **y** and there is a **consonant before it**, change the **y** to **i** and add **es**; e.g., bury → bur**ies**.

To change the verb from the present tense to the past tense, change the **y** to **i** and add **ed**; e.g., carr**y** → carr**ied**.

List **1** **Write the word.**

tried _____

flies _____

cried _____

spies _____

fried _____

dries _____

copies _____

tidied _____

studied _____

carries _____

fancies _____

worried _____

notified _____

married _____

denies _____

hurried _____

buries _____

partied _____

relied _____

empties _____

4 **Chunks.** Rearrange the chunks to make a list word.

a ie s sp _____

b fi ed ti no _____

c pa ied rt _____

d d fr ie _____

e pt ies em _____

f u die d st _____

2 **Sort the words.**

ies words

_____ _____

_____ _____

_____ _____

_____ _____

_____ _____

_____ _____

ied words

_____ _____

_____ _____

_____ _____

_____ _____

_____ _____

3 **Complete each sentence with a list word.**

a I _____ the mess in my room.

b I was _____ I had left something behind.

c The little girl always _____ her teddy bear around with her.

d The girl _____ hard for her driving test and passed with flying colors.

e He _____ out the door so he wouldn't miss his bus.

f My uncle and aunt have been _____ to each other for years.

L.3.1.D Form and use regular and irregular verbs.

Verb endings: ies, ied

1 **Revise your spelling list from page 104.** Which list word means?

a Attempted _____

b Likes or attracted to _____

c Refuses to agree with _____

d To have trusted or depended on _____

e Moves through the air using wings _____

f To have shed tears _____

Challenge words

2 **Write the word.**

supplies _____

replied _____

queries _____

applies _____

qualifies _____

purified _____

remedied _____

occupies _____

satisfied _____

identified _____

3 **Hidden words.** Find the challenge word.

a yheequalifiestoqu _____

b syusatisfiedbusj _____

c uyadappliesbhai _____

d xualoccupiesbyua _____

e poenpurifiedupaq _____

f stamsupplieskgiuu _____

g eyidentifiedoiyn _____

h aserepliedkjbu _____

i opiremedieduoya _____

j apqueriesqrsl _____

4 **Another way to say it.** Which challenge word could replace the underlined word?

a The medicine <u>cured</u> his headache. _____

b The company <u>provides</u> food for the homeless. _____

c The bird watcher <u>recognized</u> the bird. _____

d Tony <u>responded</u> to the email. _____

e Sarah <u>questions</u> whether to go to the party. _____

f The armchair <u>fills</u> a corner of the room. _____

End punctuation

Sentences can end with a **period** (.), **exclamation point** (!), or **question mark** (?), e.g., The children are playing. What are they doing? How good is that!

1 **Fill in the punctuation marks.**

   a His name is Felix   b I don't think so

   c Where does he live   d How weird is that

   e What an amazing house   f Where have they gone

   g Knock on the door   h I'll write them a note

   i Is anyone at home   j Put it in the mailbox

2 **Match the sentence to the picture.**

a    b    c

  (Put it away.)   (What's it about?)   (What a surprise!)

3 **Write the question.**

  Q: How many fingers do you have?   **A:** I have eight fingers.

  a **Q:** _____

      A: My dad is in the shed.

  b **Q:** _____

      A: Roald Dahl wrote *Revolting Rhymes*.

  c **Q:** _____

      A: We are meeting them at three o'clock.

  L.3.2 Demonstrate command of the conventions of standard English capitalization, punctuation, and spelling when writing.

Wally the Water Dragon

Finding facts and information

To find facts and information in a text, ask the questions **Who? What? Where?** or **When?** The answers can be clearly seen in the text.

Read the passage.

Underline the phrase that tells us where the frogs lived.

Circle what frogs' eggs become when they hatch.

Highlight the sound frogs make.

Once upon a time, we used to have lots of frogs living in our pond. We watched their eggs hatch into tadpoles. The frogs croaked a chorus to us every night. They were especially loud when it rained.

We don't have frogs anymore. We have dragons instead. The dragons ate the frogs' eggs, the tadpoles, and the baby frogs. So the big frogs hopped away to find a safer home.

We still have big goldfish living in our pond. The dragons don't eat the adult goldfish, but I think they eat the babies.

Color when the frogs croaked especially loudly.

Put a box around the pronoun that shows who thinks the dragons eat the baby goldfish.

Circle the correct answer for each question.

1 **Where** did the frogs used to live?

a   beside the river
c   beneath the window

b   among the flowers
d   in the pond

2 **What** do frogs' eggs hatch into?

a   goldfish
b   dragons
c   tadpoles
d   baby frogs

3 **What** did the frogs do every night?

a   croak
b   swim
c   sleep
d   play

4 **When** did the frogs croak the loudest?

a   at night
b   in the morning
c   when it rained
d   in the summer

5 **Who** thinks the dragons eat the baby goldfish?

a   the adult goldfish
b   the narrator
c   the big frogs
d   the baby frogs

Wally the Water Dragon

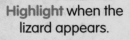

Read the passage.

Underline the blue-tongue lizard's home.

(Circle) the key word that tells us how the blue-tongue lizard catches insects.

A fat blue-tongue lizard lives under the garage box on our balcony. He comes out when the sun shines and flicks his long, blue tongue, trying to catch insects.

Possums hiss in the night and rustle through the trees. They are heading for the banana palms at the back of the house, hoping to find a bunch of ripe bananas for a feast.

Highlight when the lizard appears.

Color the possums' nighttime behavior.

1 **Where** does the blue-tongue lizard live?

_____

_____

2 **When** does the blue-tongue lizard come out of its home?

_____

_____

3 **How** does the blue-tongue lizard catch insects?

_____

_____

4 **What** do the possums do at night?

_____

_____

5 **Where** are the banana palms?

_____

RL.3.1 Ask and answer questions to demonstrate understanding of a text, referring explicitly to the text as the basis for the answers.

augh and ough

The letters **augh** make the single sound **aw**; e.g., c**augh**t.

The letters **ough** make the single sound **aw** and other sounds; e.g., b**ough**t.

List ① **Write the word.**

laugh _____

ought _____

bought _____

caught _____

fought _____

taught _____

though _____

brought _____

thought _____

through _____

naughty _____

cough _____

enough _____

rough _____

laughter _____

dough _____

tough _____

plough _____

daughter _____

drought _____

② **Complete the word with *augh* or *ough*.**

a l_____

b d_____

c th_____t

d t_____t

③ **In a group.** Write the list word that belongs in each group.

a bring, bringing, _____

b catch, catching, _____

c laugh, laughing, _____

d think, thinking, _____

e teach, teaching, _____

f buy, buying, _____

④ **Meaning.** Which list word means?

a In one end and out the other _____

b Flour and water that is baked into bread _____

c To have purchased an item _____

d To release air noisily from the lungs _____

e A person's female child _____

f Uneven or bumpy _____

L.3.2.F Use spelling patterns and generalizations in writing words.

augh and ough

1 **Revise your spelling list from page 109.** Underline the mistake. Write the word correctly.

a Two strong horses pulled the plaugh through the fields. _____

b The police cought the thieves red-handed. _____

c My mother is my grandfather's doughter. _____

d Micky was very noughty to put paint all over the walls. _____

e Sue had a nasty caugh when she was sick. _____

f Ling thaught that the time at the park was too short. _____

g We mixed flour and water to make daugh. _____

h There was not enaugh food to go around. _____

i I had to lough at my brother's impression of a pigeon. _____

Challenge words

2 **Write the word.**

bough _____

draught _____

sought _____

throughout _____

thorough _____

trough _____

wrought _____

haughty _____

onslaught _____

distraught _____

3 **Complete the sentence.**

a The pig ate at the _____.

b We searched _____ the house but couldn't find the ball.

c They hung a swing from a _____ on the tree.

d They _____ advice from their parents.

e The _____ iron gate slammed shut behind them.

f The cleaners did a _____ clean of the whole house.

4 **Word clues.** Which challenge word means?

a a current of air in a room _____

b anxiously worried or upset _____

c a forceful, sudden attack _____

L.3.2.F Use spelling patterns and generalizations in writing words.

Abstract nouns

An **abstract noun** names a thought, quality or feeling. We cannot see, hear or touch it; e.g., idea, kindness, happiness.

1 **Circle the abstract noun in each pair.**

a weakness legs	**b** fire warmth	**c** love puppy	**d** chocolate delight
e sadness tears	**f** princess beauty	**g** length ruler	**h** dictator cruelty
i fun movie	**j** tooth pain	**k** bread hunger	**l** energy child

2 **Complete each phrase with an abstract noun from the list.**

sweetness   softness   sourness   hardness

a   the _____ of fur
b   the _____ of a rock
c   the _____ of honey
d   the _____ of a lemon

3 **Find the matching pairs.**

a   idea   wickedness

b   fun   anxiety

c   evil   knowledge

d   worry   thought

e   information   enjoyment

4 **Change the word in bold to a noun.**
If someone is:

a   **strong**, they have _____.

b   **healthy**, they have good _____.

c   **happy**, they have _____.

d   **curious**, they show _____.

e   **courageous**, they have _____.

f   **patient**, they have a lot of _____.

g   **imaginative**, they have _____.

h   **miserable**, they experience _____.

i   **celebrating**, they are having a _____.

j   **sympathetic**, they feel _____ for others.

bright

brightness

Yellow-bellied Goalie

Point of view
To identify point of view, look at the way characters act and feel. The clues are in the way they express their opinions (what they think and believe) and views about a subject.

Read the passage.

Circle the word that means the same as *scared*.

Underline Ben's thoughts.

Highlight the sentence that tells us what Ben thought of himself.

Color the word that is similar in meaning to *run away from*.

Ben unpacked the goalie gear from the bag. He pulled on the heavy chest plate, the green-colored leg pads, and the bright orange foot kickers. He put on the safety helmet.

"OK Ben, you're ready for battle," said Coach.

Battle? That's what it was all right.

Ben couldn't move. He was afraid to move. He stood like a statue. He wanted to run away. The only trouble was he could barely walk in his leg pads, let alone run.

He'd be the biggest joke in the team. A giant, padded chicken, trying to escape its fate.

Circle the correct answer for each question.

1 How did Ben **feel** about playing goalie? He was …
   a excited.   b angry.   c scared.   d happy.

2 Which is the best **clue** to how Ben felt?
   a He couldn't move.   b He felt like a statue.
   c He was ready for battle.   d He wanted to run away.

3 In Ben's **view**, what kind of goalie would he make?
   a a bad one   b a good one   c a brave one   d a strong one

4 Which phrase helps you see Ben's **view**? He said …
   a he'd try his best.   b he'd be the biggest joke in the team.
   c he'd act like a giant, padded chicken.   d he could barely walk in his leg pads.

Yellow-bellied Goalie

Read the passage.

Underline the sentences that show what Ben's teammates said to him.

Highlight a phrase that shows that Ben was proud of himself.

Circle the word that describes the kind of goalie Ben thought he was before.

Color two adjectives that describe the kind of goalie Ben thinks he is now.

The umpire blew the whistle. The game was over.

"You're a great goalie!" yelled David, patting Ben on the back.

"Benny, you're on fire," cheered another boy.

Ben held his head up high, held his chest out and threw his hands in the air, making high fives with his team.

Ben had done it. He had gone from yellow-bellied to big brave goalie, and it hadn't hurt a bit.

Being a goalie wasn't so bad after all. Maybe, just maybe, he'd give it another go next week.

1. From the **point of view** of Ben's teammates, what kind of goalie is he?

_____

_____

2. In your own words, explain how Ben's **opinion** of himself as a goalie has changed.

_____

_____

_____

3. How does Ben **feel** about playing goalie in the future?

_____

_____

Suffix: ed

> To show that something has already happened, we sometimes add the suffix **ed** to the verb; e.g., walk**ed**. When the verb ends in a consonant that has a <u>short vowel before</u> it, **double the consonant** before adding **ed**; e.g., gr<u>a</u>b → gra**bb**ed.

List ① **Write the word.**

batted _____

fanned _____

tapped _____

ripped _____

hopped _____

petted _____

jutted _____

rotted _____

sobbed _____

hummed _____

slipped _____

shopped _____

chipped _____

drummed _____

snapped _____

wrapped _____

grinned _____

dragged _____

spotted _____

slammed _____

② **Double the last letter then add *ed*.**

a   tap _____

b   wrap _____

c   drum _____

d   hop _____

e   jut _____

f   snap _____

g   slip _____

h   sob _____

i   drag _____

j   slam _____

③ **In a group.** Write the list word that belongs in each group.

a   knocked, rapped, _____

b   cloaked, enveloped, _____

c   shut, banged, _____

d   slid, tripped, _____

e   stained, decayed, _____

f   blew, cooled, _____

④ **Meaning.** Which list word means?

a   Stuck out sharply _____

b   Patted or stroked an animal _____

c   To have hit the ball in baseball _____

d   Made a singing sound without opening the lips _____

e   Smiled broadly _____

f   A small piece has broken off something _____

g   Decomposed or decayed _____

L.3.1.E Form and use the simple verb tenses.

Suffix: ed

1 **Revise your spelling list from page 114.** Fill in the missing word.

a I _____ a hole in my pants when I jumped over the fence.

b The frog _____ around the edge of the pond before diving in.

c The edge of the tea cup was _____ after I dropped it.

d We _____ all day, but I still didn't find a dress for the party.

e I put my arms around her and hugged her as she _____.

f I _____ a rhythm on my bongo drums.

g I _____ twigs in half so we could put them on the fire.

h When she _____ I could see her small white teeth.

Challenge words

2 **Write the word.**

stripped _____

admitted _____

scrapped _____

permitted _____

equipped _____

shredded _____

transmitted _____

programmed _____

embedded _____

acquitted _____

3 **Complete the sentence.**

a He _____ to eating the whole cake.

b She was _____ and ready to go camping.

c Mom _____ the sheets off the bed.

d My brother _____ his computer to wake him up each morning.

e Dad _____ me to have a bowl of ice cream.

f The thorn was _____ in his foot.

g The man was _____ of the crime.

4 **Another way to say it.** Which challenge word could replace the underlined word.

a They <u>discarded</u> their original idea and started again.
_____

b The man was <u>freed</u> of the charge of theft.
_____

c The TV show was <u>transferred</u> from a small studio.
_____

d My brother <u>tore</u> the lettuce for the tacos.
_____

Pronoun-antecedent agreement

> **Pronouns** stand in place of nouns. They save us repeating nouns; e.g., **Jack** put on **Jack's** hat. **Jack** put on **his** hat. Pronouns must agree with the nouns they refer to (the antecedent).

1 **Complete each sentence with the correct pronoun.**

a Cindy and I have completed _____ tasks. | us | our |

b The children are putting on _____ hats. | their | they |

c I asked the girl if _____ knew the answer. | her | she |

d When I stuck the pin into the balloon, _____ burst. | my | it |

e I called to my friends when I saw _____ in the park. | them | they |

2 **Replace the nouns in parentheses with pronouns.**

a Tim let me play with (Tim's) _____ puppy.

b Mom made Gina promise that (Gina) _____ would do her violin practice.

c I told Dad that I would help (Dad) _____ tidy the garage.

d The patients have put (the patients') _____ trust in the doctor.

e My friend and I said that (my friend and I) _____ would wash the dishes.

3 **In each sentence, underline the pronoun and circle the noun it refers to.**

a The spectators cheered loudly when their favorite player ran onto the field.

b Rosie asked Ben to help her carry the equipment.

c The dog buried its bone in one of the flower beds.

d Bubbles burst when they fly too high.

e Simon blinked when the light shone in his eyes.

L.3.1.F Ensure pronoun-antecedent agreement.

How Owl Got His Feathers

Read the passage.

When the world was young, Owl did not have feathers. One day, all the world's birds decided to hold a grand ball.

"How can I go?" sighed Owl. "All the other birds will wear fine suits to the ball. I have no feathers, and they'll make fun of me."

Hawk heard what Owl had said, and he told the other birds. Every bird gave Hawk a feather, and Hawk passed the feathers to Owl.

Underline the key words in each text that show why the main characters need a special outfit.

Highlight the key words in each text that show why the main characters can't go to the special event.

Color the key words in each text that show who helped the main characters.

Cinderella gazed sadly at the dying embers in the fireplace. Her stepsister's cruel words rang through her head.

"You can't possibly come with us to the grand ball. Everyone will laugh at you in those miserable rags!"

"But you can go to the ball," said a kind voice. Cinderella gave a start. "I am your fairy godmother," continued the voice, "and I will give you a fine silk gown to wear."

Circle the correct answers.

1 What are the connections between the texts?

a The main characters have only rags to wear.

b The main characters want to go to a ball.

c The main characters are birds.

d The main characters are given fine silk gowns to wear.

e The main characters don't have suitable outfits to wear to a ball.

f The main characters are sitting in front of a fireplace.

g Kind strangers help the main characters.

h The main characters are afraid that people will make fun of them.

How Owl Got His Feathers

Read the passage.

Owl was so pleased! He flew proudly to the ball.

Owl was having such a wonderful time that he didn't want to give the feathers back, so he silently flew away and hid amongst the trees in the forest.

When the party was over, the other birds looked for Owl, but they could not find him. His new feathers helped him blend into the environment.

Now, Owl only comes out to hunt at night, when the other birds are sleeping.

Circle the word in each text that shows what owls are covered in.

Underline the words in each text that tell us what owls do during the day.

Highlight the words in each text that show how an owl's feathers help to protect it.

Color the words in each text that tell us what owls do at night.

There are around 200 different owl species. They are nocturnal, which means they are active at night. During the day, they stay hidden in trees.

Most owls hunt insects, small mammals, and other birds. Some species hunt fish. Their powerful talons, or claws, help them catch and kill their prey.

Compared to other birds of prey, owls are very quiet in flight. They are hard to spot during the day. Their feathers have a pattern that helps them blend in with the environment.

1 Use the information in the texts to write a short report about owls. Use the headings provided.

Owls

a Covering: _____

_____

b Daytime activities: _____

_____

c Nocturnal activities: _____

_____

d Camouflage: _____

_____

RL.3.1 Ask and answer questions to demonstrate understanding of a text, referring explicitly to the text as the basis for the answers.

Soft c and g

> The letter **c** makes a soft **s** sound when it comes before **e**, **i** or **y**; e.g., **c**enter, pen**c**il, i**c**y. Before the vowels **a**, **o**, **u** and some consonants, it makes a **k** sound; e.g., **c**astle, **c**old, **c**ut.
>
> Sometimes the letter **g** makes a soft **j** sound when it comes before **e**, **i** or **y**; e.g., **g**entle, **g**iraffe, **g**ym. Sometimes it makes its own sound of **g**; e.g., **g**ift.

List **1** **Write the word.**

gym _____

city _____

circus _____

giant _____

pencil _____

rice _____

magic _____

stage _____

huge _____

danger _____

orange _____

dance _____

village _____

engine _____

giraffe _____

grace _____

cycle _____

circle _____

angel _____

since _____

2 **Unscramble these list words.**

a lilvgae _____

b grnaoe _____

c gffriae _____

d cclye _____

e angerd _____

3 **Sort the words.**

soft c

_____ _____

_____ _____

_____ _____

_____ _____

soft g

_____ _____

_____ _____

_____ _____

_____ _____

_____ _____

4 **Name.**

a _____ b _____ c _____ d _____

Soft c and g

1 **Revise your spelling list from page 119.** Find the list word that fits.

a   a place people visit to get fit and healthy   _____

b   used to power a car   _____

c   something performed by a magician   _____

d   a larger than normal human   _____

e   a platform used for performances   _____

f   something that could cause harm   _____

g   a small town   _____

Challenge words

2 **Write the word.**

sentence   _____

lettuce   _____

intelligence   _____

embrace   _____

image   _____

general   _____

citizen   _____

garbage   _____

emergency   _____

cylinder   _____

3 **Hidden words.** Find the challenge word.

a   euixintelligenceuegf   _____

b   golsdcitizensfosr   _____

c   sdfsentencebsowj   _____

d   lomagarbageyeln   _____

e   sabemergencyishk   _____

f   pltsimagehiklao   _____

4 **Word clues.** Which challenge word matches?

a   trash   _____

b   a vegetable   _____

c   a 3D shape   _____

5 **Complete the sentence.**

a   One of his chores is to take out the _____.

b   A _____ begins with a capital letter and ends with a period.

c   They called the ambulance as it was an _____.

d   He chopped the _____ for the salad.

e   The scientist is a person of great _____.

f   Ranjit was a _____ of two countries.

L.3.2.F Use spelling patterns and generalizations in writing words.

Adverbs of time

Adverbs give information about verbs. **Adverbs of time** tell when or how often an action happens; e.g., now, yesterday, soon.

1 Circle the word that tells when something happens.

a I woke up earlier.

b They will be here later.

c We should be home soon.

d I am going to the movies tomorrow.

e I immediately took him to the doctor.

f He sometimes forgets to do his chores.

g I always wear a hat.

2 Match the words that are opposite in meaning.

a earlier   nightly

b always   after

c daily   last

d sometimes   never

e first   later

f before   often

3

Is this something we should do often, sometimes, or never?

_____

4 Fill in the adverbs.

I am going to my friend's house **a** _____.

I have been there many times **b** _____. We

c _____ have lots of fun. **d** _____

we go to the park, but **e** _____ we play in his yard.

When we are together, we **f** _____ get bored!

usually

before

never

tomorrow

sometimes

always

L.3.1.A Explain the function of adverbs in general and their functions in particular sentences.

121

Monsters

Read the passage.

Circle the name of Japan's favorite monster.

Underline the phrase that tells us where Godzilla used to live.

Big things are big trouble. Enormous monsters cause chaos and destruction wherever they go. Godzilla is Japan's favorite monster. He first blasted onto Japanese movie screens in 1954 and he's still there today. Godzilla slept on the bottom of the sea until an atomic bomb forced him up to the surface. He looks like a giant *Tyrannosaurus rex* having a temper tantrum. He is angry because he thinks people are destroying the world.

Highlight the year of the first Godzilla movie.

Color the words that describe Godzilla's appearance.

Circle the correct answer for each question.

1 **Who** is Japan's favorite monster?
   a   a giant
   b   a dinosaur
   c   Tyrannosaurus rex
   d   Godzilla

2 **When** did Japan's favorite monster first appear on movie screens?
   a   1945
   b   1954
   c   1956
   d   1964

3 **Where** did Godzilla live before he was forced into the world?
   a   on an island
   b   in a forest
   c   on the bottom of the sea
   d   in the sky

4 **What** does Godzilla look like?
   a   a huge *Tyrannosaurus rex*
   b   a giant
   c   an angry monster
   d   a sea monster

RI.3.1 Ask and answer questions to demonstrate understanding of a text, referring explicitly to the text as the basis for the answers.

Monsters

Read the passage.

Read the full text Monsters

The World of Monsters

Every country has its own stories, or myths, about monsters. Monsters were a good way to explain the unknown. If people didn't know what caused an earthquake, for example, they could say a monster did it.

When Native Americans first dug up dinosaur bones, they thought they were the bones of giant lizards that lived deep in the earth. When these giants shivered, the whole earth quaked!

Many myths tell of monsters with terrible powers. Medusa had snakes instead of hair. Anyone who looked at her was turned to stone. But the hero Perseus was able to defeat her by looking at her reflection in a mirror. Every monster has a weak spot. The trick is to find out where, or what, it is.

Underline the words that tell us why people tell monster stories.

Highlight what Native Americans believed dinosaur bones to be.

Circle words that describe Medusa's appearance.

Color Medusa's terrible power.

Underline the actions of Perseus.

Circle the key to defeating monsters.

1 **What** are monster myths used for? _____

_____

2 **Where** do we find monster myths? _____

3 **What** was Medusa's terrible power? _____

_____

4 **Who** defeated Medusa? _____

5 **What** will help you defeat any monster? _____

_____

RI.3.1 Ask and answer questions to demonstrate understanding of a text, referring explicitly to the text as the basis for the answers.

123

Irregular past tense verbs

Irregular verbs do not have the suffix **ed** in the past tense. Some irregular verbs change their spelling and sound different in the past tense; e.g., grow → grew. Some irregular verbs *do not* change their spelling or sound different in the past tense; e.g., cost.

List **1** **Write the word.**

broke _____

blew _____

told _____

slept _____

shook _____

began _____

became _____

chose _____

wrote _____

found _____

froze _____

knew _____

heard _____

awoke _____

bled _____

slung _____

meant _____

struck _____

hidden _____

mistook _____

2 **Chunks.**

Rearrange the letters to make a list word.

a se o ch _____

b en hi dd _____

c ar he d _____

d oo sh k _____

e ew bl _____

f ew kn _____

g ea m nt _____

h ck st ru _____

3 **In a group.** Write the list word that belongs in each group.

a sleep, sleeping, _____

b know, knowing, _____

c strike, striking, _____

d bleed, bleeding, _____

e find, finding, _____

f begin, begun, _____

g choose, choosing, _____

h break, breaking, _____

4 **Meaning.** Which list word means?

a To have started something _____

b To have understood incorrectly _____

c To have discovered something _____

d To have received sound through the ears _____

e To have sent out air from the mouth _____

f To have picked one or more from a group _____

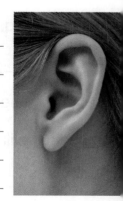

L.3.1.E Form and use the simple verb tenses.

Irregular past tense verbs

1 **Revise your spelling list from page 124.** Write the past tense of the word in parentheses.

a I (awake) _____ early this morning.

b Yesterday I (hear) _____ a noise next door.

c Last week I (break) _____ Mom's flower pot.

d She has already (tell) _____ me the truth.

e Last night I (sleep) _____ in my brother's room.

f I (begin) _____ karate lessons last week.

g The girl (become) _____ sick after eating bad food.

Challenge words

2 **Write the word.**

shone _____

knelt _____

dealt _____

built _____

spread _____

forgave _____

understood _____

withdrew _____

forbade _____

broadcast _____

3 **Hidden words.** Find the challenge word.

a asforgaveuoasgh _____

b abroadcastawoih _____

c sihslungusyk _____

d asyigforbadeough _____

e asuokneltushap _____

f asdunderstoodiu _____

4 **Word clues.** Which challenge word means?

a reflected light _____

b made or created _____

c prohibited _____

5 **Another way to say it.** Which challenge word could replace the underlined word?

a The men <u>created</u> the cubby house over two days. _____

b The TV channel stopped the <u>transmission</u>. _____

c The moon <u>glowed</u> in the dark night sky. _____

d They <u>excused</u> the child's bad behavior as he was tired. _____

e The bird <u>stretched</u> its wings and flew away. _____

Apostrophes for contractions

Apostrophes can show where letters are missing in a word; e.g.,
do not → don't. Words with missing letters are called **contractions**.

1 **Fill in the apostrophes.**

a She wont eat it.

b I dont think so.

c You mustnt go there!

d I think its my turn.

e They havent arrived yet.

f Those arent mine.

g He doesnt know them.

h Ill write them a note

i Ill see you tomorrow.

j You shouldve seen her!

2 **Match the words.**

a have not   can't

b could have   won't

c will not   might've

d cannot   could've

e might have   haven't

3 **Write the contraction.**

a let us _____

b do not _____

c did not _____

d she is _____

e we will _____

4 **Sort the sentences.**

It isn't here.
We weren't upset.
I can't do it.
She couldn't go.
They aren't happy.
He wasn't there.

Present tense

_____
_____
_____

Past tense

_____
_____
_____

L.3.2 Demonstrate command of the conventions of standard punctuation when writing.

Flowers

Read the passages.

Many animals feed on the nectar from flowers. As a result, the animals carry pollen from flower to flower.

Many insects feed on flowers. Flowers have color and perfume to attract insects. As insects feed on the nectar, they also pick up some pollen. The pollen catches a ride to the next flower. After being pollinated, flowers make seeds.

Birds, bats, and even some lizards are also attracted to flowers.

Circle the word in each text that tells us what insects feed on.

Underline the words in each text that tell us what attracts insects to certain flowers.

Highlight the word in each text that tells us what insects carry from flower to flower.

Color the words in each text that tell us what flowers produce after they have been pollinated.

Pollination is an important part of the life cycle of plants. Insects such as bees, butterflies, and ladybugs are attracted by the bright colors and smells of certain flowers. They know that these flowers contain the sweet nectar that they need to grow and lay eggs. While sucking the nectar, some of the pollen on the flowers sticks to their legs. This pollen gets transferred to the next flower they move to. The pollen fertilizes the flower's egg cells to make seeds.

Circle the correct answers.

1 What do both texts tell us?

a   Many insects feed on the nectar from flowers.

b   The bright colors and perfumes of plants help to attract insects.

c   Insects lay their eggs in flowers.

d   Insects play an important role in pollination.

e   Bees and butterflies need nectar to grow and lay eggs.

f   Some flowers grow into fruits.

g   Insects carry pollen from flower to flower.

h   Flowers make seeds after they have been pollinated.

i   Birds and other animals also play a role in pollination.

Flowers

Read the full text

Flowers

Read the passages.

Flowering plants are able to live in many different parts of the world. Rain forests, deserts, and cold mountains are all home to different flowering plants.

Rain forests get plenty of what plants need—rain, warmth, and sunshine—so plants grow in great numbers. A huge variety of flowering plants, such as trees, vines, and other tropical plants, grow in rain forests.

Underline all the words in both texts that refer to the climate in rainforests.

Highlight all the words in both texts that refer to the number of plants found in rainforests.

Rain forests cover about 6% of the earth's surface but contain more than half of the world's plant and animal species.

Rain forests have hot, humid climates. They also have a very high annual rainfall. That's why they are called rain forests!

At least two-thirds of the world's plant species grow in rain forests.

1 Use the information in the texts to write a short report about rain forests. Use the headings provided.

Rain forests

a Climate: _____

_____

_____

_____

b Plants: _____

_____

_____

_____

RI.3.1 Ask and answer questions to demonstrate understanding of a text, referring explicitly to the text as the basis for the answers.

Endings: ery, ary, ory

Many words that end in **ery**, **ary**, and **ory** have a similar end sound; e.g., bakery, salary, victory.

List ① Write the word.

bakery _____

cookery _____

diary _____

bravery _____

factory _____

greenery _____

salary _____

misery _____

grocery _____

victory _____

battery _____

burglary _____

memory _____

mystery _____

delivery _____

library _____

nursery _____

summary _____

crockery _____

glossary _____

② Sort the words.

ary words

_____ _____

_____ _____

_____ _____

_____ _____

_____ _____

ery words

_____ _____

_____ _____

_____ _____

_____ _____

_____ _____

ory words

_____ _____

_____ _____

_____ _____

_____ _____

_____ _____

③ Complete the word with *ery*, *ory* or *ary*.

a batt_____   b gloss_____

c mis_____   d crock_____

e green_____   f summ_____

g cook_____   h groc_____

i burgl_____   j bak_____

Endings: ery, ary, ory

1 **Revise your spelling list from page 129.** Match the word to the clue.

a   a book in which you write your thoughts and feelings _____

b   a building where items are produced _____

c   a set amount of money paid regularly for work _____

d   a win _____

e   the ability to remember _____

f   something that cannot be explained _____

g   a place where you can go to read and borrow books _____

h   a room for babies or young children _____

Challenge words

2 **Write the word.**

ordinary _____

discovery _____

territory _____

upholstery _____

vocabulary _____

imaginary _____

category _____

dictionary _____

laboratory _____

necessary _____

3 **Analogy.** Complete the analogy with a challenge word.

a   Front is to back as hiding is to

_____

b   Flat is to round as unnecessary is to

_____

c   Black is to white as irregular is to

_____

d   On is to off as real is to

_____

e   House is to home as word is to

_____

4 **Another way to say it.** Which challenge word could replace the underlined word?

a   They moved from one <u>district</u> to another. _____

b   We bought a gift even though it wasn't <u>needed</u>. _____

c   She studied the Japanese <u>words</u> carefully. _____

d   My sister received first prize in her age <u>division</u> this season. _____

e   Wednesday was a completely <u>normal</u> day this week. _____

L.3.2.F Use spelling patterns and generalizations in writing words.

Prepositions

Prepositions show the relationship between nouns or pronouns and other words in a sentence. They tell **when, where, how,** or **why**; e.g., I will meet you **at** midday. The milk is **in** the fridge. They traveled **by** bus. She did it **for** them.

1 **Does the underlined preposition show WHEN, WHERE, HOW, or WHY?**

a I woke up <u>before</u> sunrise.   _____

b I have just come <u>from</u> the shops.   _____

c We should be home <u>by</u> six o'clock.   _____

d I immediately took him <u>to</u> the doctor.   _____

e She ate her food <u>with</u> a knife and fork. _____

f I made the card <u>for</u> her.   _____

2 **Complete the crossword puzzle.**

Across:
1 Six comes _____ five.
3 I will meet you _____ the movies.
5 Five comes _____ six.
6 He walked _____ the road.
7 The milk is _____ the fridge.
8 They are sitting _____ an umbrella.
9 I am going _____ school.

Down:
2 I saw him _____ the window.
4 Your dog is bigger _____ mine.
5 I sat _____ her on the bus.
8 I waited _____ the end.

Deserts

Cause and effect
To find cause and effect, ask why something happens and what the result is.

Read the passage.

(Circle) the reason large desert animals are able to stay cool.

Underline the effect a fur covering has on a large desert animal's body temperature.

Desert animals conserve water. They try to avoid very hot and very cold temperatures.

The fur or hair of large desert animals keeps them cool. The outer layer of a camel's coat can be 80°F hotter than its body.

Some desert animals, such as the marsupial mole, burrow underground to escape extreme temperatures. It is cooler underground in hot deserts. In cold deserts, it is warmer underground.

Highlight what the marsupial mole does to stay cool.

Color the key word that tells why animals in cold deserts might burrow underground.

Circle the correct answer for each question.

1 What **causes** large desert animals to stay cool?

   a their skin   b their fur   c their tails   d river breezes

2 How does a desert animal's hair or fur **affect** its body temperature?

   a It keeps it warm.   b It causes it to overheat.

   c It keeps it cool.   d It causes it to freeze.

3 **Why** is the marsupial mole able to stay cool in the desert?

   a It burrows underground.   b It lies in the shade.

   c It drinks lots of water.   d It sprays water on itself.

4 What **effect** does burrowing underground have on the marsupial mole?
It enables it to ...

   a stay warm.   b find water.   c find food.   d stay cool.

RI.3.3 Describe the relationship between a series of historical events, scientific ideas or concepts, or steps in technical procedures in a text, using language that pertains to time, sequence, and cause/effect.

Deserts

Read the **full text**

Deserts

Read the passage.

Put a box around the key word that tells us what drilling and mining do to desert environments.

Circle the word that tells us who causes damage to desert water supplies.

Color the words that show how farm animals damage desert environments.

Deserts often contain oil and iron ore. Drilling for oil and mining can harm desert environments.

Tourists can damage desert water supplies. Vehicles damage desert soils and plants.

When farms are on the edge of a desert, they can damage the fragile desert soil.

Farm animals pound the soil with their hooves. This breaks up the soil. It is then more likely to be eroded by wind and rain.

Highlight the effect vehicles have on desert environments.

Color the effect farms have on desert environments.

Underline what happens when farm animals break up desert soil.

1 What human activities **cause** damage to desert environments?

_____

_____

_____

2 What **effect** do tourists have on deserts?

_____

_____

_____

3 Explain how farm animals **cause** damage to desert soils.

_____

_____

_____

RI.3.3 Describe the relationship between a series of historical events, scientific ideas or concepts, or steps in technical procedures in a text, using language that pertains to time, sequence, and cause/effect.

133

Suffixes: ful, less

Adding the suffix **ful** to a noun or verb turns it into an adjective; e.g., harm**ful**, power**ful**.

Adding the suffix **less** to a noun or verb turns it into an adjective; e.g., end**less**, care**less**.

List ① **Write the word.**

painful _____

endless _____

helpful _____

restless _____

useful _____

homeless _____

thankful _____

careless _____

hopeful _____

harmless _____

beautiful _____

thoughtful _____

blameless _____

forgetful _____

truthful _____

fearless _____

powerful _____

awful _____

tasteless _____

skilful _____

② **Sort the words.**

ful	*less*
_____	_____
_____	_____
_____	_____
_____	_____
_____	_____
_____	_____
_____	_____
_____	_____
_____	_____
_____	_____

③ **Meaning.** Which list word means?

a   Not able to relax   _____

b   Having or using force   _____

c   Causing pain   _____

d   Very bad or terrible   _____

④ **Underline the spelling mistake.** Write the word correctly.

a   During the long drive I was very restles and couldn't sit still. _____

b   The Internet is a usefull tool when researching new places to visit. _____

c   We found a homeles dog and took it to the animal shelter. _____

d   The careles driver ran a red light because he wasn't looking. _____

e   Henry is a truthfull person, who never lies. _____

f   The firefighter was fearles as he ran into a burning building. _____

L.3.2.E Use conventional spelling for high-frequency and other studied words and for adding suffixes to base words.

Suffixes: ful, less

1 **Revise your spelling list from page 134.** Rearrange the letters to make a list word.

a ss ta le ste _____

b in ful pa _____

c ho ful pe _____

d dl ss en e _____

e lp ful he _____

f le rm ss ha _____

Challenge words

2 **Write the word.**

goalless _____

worthless _____

sorrowful _____

delightful _____

weightless _____

wonderful _____

successful _____

doubtful _____

respectful _____

pointless _____

3 **Hidden words.** Find the challenge word.

a lodelightfuliohc _____

b fulpointlesshsgbeu _____

c hsirngoallessssuje _____

d dynweightlessahout _____

e csycworthlessuioet _____

f aisudgsuccessfulah _____

4 **Word clues.** Which challenge word means?

a very sad _____

b being polite _____

c doing well _____

d excellent or amazing _____

e not likely or probable _____

5 **Another way to say it.** Which challenge word could replace the underlined word?

a Emma was always <u>considerate</u> of her parents' wishes. _____

b He was a <u>prosperous</u> businessman who worked very hard. _____

c The dessert was rich and <u>delicious</u>. _____

d Chen was <u>uncertain</u> about the whole idea. _____

L.3.2.E Use conventional spelling for high-frequency and other studied words and for adding suffixes to base words.

135

Adverbial phrases

A **phrase** is a part of a sentence that has more than one word. An **adverbial phrase** does the work of an **adverb**; e.g., He dropped his sock **on the floor**.

1 **Does the underlined phrase tell WHERE, WHEN, HOW, or WHY?**

a The campers woke up <u>before sunrise</u>. _____

b They arrived <u>at the campsite</u> yesterday. _____

c The match was canceled <u>because of the rain</u>. _____

d She read the instructions <u>in a clear voice</u>. _____

e They are planting more trees <u>in the park</u>. _____

f They traveled to the match <u>by bus and train</u>. _____

2 **Fill in the adverbial phrases.**

with both hands	after midnight	around the track

a The athletes are running _____.

b We arrived home _____.

c He was banging on the door _____.

3 **Underline the adverbial phrases in these sentences.**

a Jack and Jill went up the hill.

b Humpty Dumpty sat on a wall.

c Cinderella had to be home before midnight.

d The cow jumped over the moon.

e The dish ran away with the spoon.

L.3.1.A Explain the function of adverbs in general and their functions in particular sentences.

Media

Read the passage.

Highlight the words that help you see how the Internet started in the 1960s.

Underline the words that help you see how the Internet spread.

Color the words that help you see how people use the Internet today.

In the 1960s, a few large computers in the USA connected to each other.

If one of the computers broke down, the others would keep working. Universities began to connect computers in the same way. This grew into the Internet—lots of computers connected to each other.

The Internet spread as more people were allowed to use it. Thousands and then millions of computers went online around the world. The speed at which the Internet sent information got much faster.

Today, billions of people use the Internet to find and share information, for entertainment, and to buy and sell goods.

1 Read the passage again. As you do so, visualize what you are reading about. Draw pictures of the different stages in the growth of the Internet.

a The start of the Internet— the 1960s	b More people are allowed to use the Internet

RI.3.1 Ask and answer questions to demonstrate understanding of a text, referring explicitly to the text as the basis for the answers.

137

Media

Read the passage.

Read the full text

Medic

A storyboard artist turns a film script into a series of drawings to help the people making the story imagine what it is going to look like.

Script for a short film about Humpty Dumpty

Scene 1: *Humpty Dumpty is sitting on the castle wall. He waves to the crowd below.*

Humpty: Hi everyone.

Humpty stands up. He loses his balance and starts toppling forward.

Humpty: Aaaaaahhhhhh!

Scene 2: *The people in the crowd look down at Humpty's cracked body. Someone takes out a phone and calls an ambulance.*

Person in crowd: (*talking on phone*) Come to the castle wall quickly. Prince Humpty's had an accident.

The paramedics patch up Humpty's cracked body.

Paramedic: You're very lucky, Prince Humpty. If the cracks had been any deeper, you would have needed a yolk transfusion.

Circle the words that help you see what Humpty does in Scene 1.

Underline the words that help you see what Humpty looks like after the accident.

Color the words that help you see what the paramedics do to Humpty.

1 Imagine you are a storyboard artist. Create a storyboard for the film about Humpty Dumpty.

a Scene 1	b Scene 2

RI.3.1 Ask and answer questions to demonstrate understanding of a text, referring explicitly to the text as the basis for the answers.

Silent t, n, u

> **Silent letters** are letters in a word that are not pronounced. The letter **t** is usually silent when it comes after **s**; e.g., fas**t**en. Sometimes the letter **n** is silent when it comes after **m**; e.g., colum**n**. The letter **u** is often silent when it is next to **another vowel**; e.g., g**u**ard, b**u**ild.

List ① **Write the word.**

listen _____
fasten _____
castle _____
often _____
build _____
guide _____
rustle _____
soften _____
nestle _____
guard _____
biscuit _____
bristle _____
thistle _____
glisten _____
Christmas _____
guess _____
moisten _____
guest _____
solemn _____
guitar _____

② **Sort the words.**

Silent *t*	Silent *n*	Silent *u*
_____	_____	_____
_____	_____	_____
_____	_____	_____
_____	_____	_____
_____	_____	_____
_____	_____	_____
_____	_____	_____
_____	_____	_____
_____	_____	_____
_____	_____	_____
_____	_____	_____
_____	_____	_____
_____	_____	_____

③ **Chunks.** Rearrange the sections to make a list word.

a st bri le _____
b ar gu it _____
c it bis cu _____
d mas Ch st ri _____

④ **Which silent letter is missing?**

a nes_____le   b mois_____en   c lis_____en   d b_____ild   e this_____le

⑤ **Name.**

a _____   b _____   c _____   d _____

Silent t, n, u

1 **Revise your spelling list from page 139.** Underline the mistake. Write the word correctly.

a I always make sure I fasen my seatbelt. _____

b The presidential inauguration was a solem occasion. _____

c I can play three chords on the gitar. _____

d I pricked my finger on a thisle. _____

e The lake would glisen when the sunlight was upon it. _____

f I took a biscit from the plate. _____

g In Paris we needed a gide to show us the sights. _____

h The leaves rusle when the wind blows. _____

Challenge words

2 **Write the word.**

whistle _____

wrestle _____

hustle _____

column _____

trestle _____

disguise _____

guilty _____

circuit _____

hymn _____

guild _____

3 **Word clues.** Which challenge word means?

a responsible for doing something wrong

_____

b a structure that looks like a post

_____

c to hide someone's appearance

_____

d to make a sound with your mouth

_____

e a song written in praise

_____

f to work swiftly

_____

4 **Complete the sentences.**

a My little brothers would _____ all day if they were allowed.

b The Earth makes a _____ around the Sun.

c The _____ is the framework that holds up the bridge.

L.3.2.F Use spelling patterns and generalizations in writing words.

Adjectival phrases

A **phrase** is a part of a sentence that has more than one word. An **adjectival phrase** does the work of an adjective; e.g., The girl **in the white hat.**

1 **Match the phrase to the picture.**

| with long hair | under an umbrella | during the night |

 a
_____
_____
_____

 b
_____
_____
_____

 c
_____
_____
_____

2 **Fill in the phrases.**

| in the smart suit | with happy endings | on the corner |

a   The man _____ is my uncle.

b   The shop _____ sells toys.

c   Stories _____ are my favorites.

3 **Match the beginnings and endings.**

a   The Wonderful Wizard   of Peter Rabbit

b   The Cat   of Oz

c   Alice's Adventures   in the Willows

d   The Tale   in the Hat

e   The Wind   in Wonderland

4 **Underline the adjectival phrase.**

The Secret of the Treasure Seekers

5 **Underline the adjectival phrases in these sentences.**

a   The girl in the blue dress is Cinderella.

b   The lady with the wand is her fairy godmother.

L.3.1.A Explain the function of adjectives in general and their functions in particular sentences.

Drama

Read the passage.

Highlight the name of the person who plays an important role in putting on a play.

In paragraph 2, circle all the verbs that tell us what the stage manager does.

Many people work as a team to put on a play. The stage manager has one of the most important jobs.

The stage manager helps the director, actors, and stage crew. They plan and run rehearsals, and set up the stage. They listen to the actors to check if they are following the script.

When the play is in performance, the stage manager is in charge. They make sure the stage lights go on and off when they need to. They check that the set changes correctly.

The smooth running of the play is the stage manager's responsibility.

Underline the things the stage manager is responsible for when a play is in performance.

Color the word that describes how the play should run.

Circle the correct answers.

1 What is the passage mainly about?

a the director's jobs
b the stage crew's jobs
c the stage manager's jobs
d the actors' jobs

2 Which three **details** support the main idea?

a People work as a team to put on a play.

b The stage manager helps the director, actors, and stage crew.

c The stage manager sets up the stage.

d The set changes between scenes.

e The stage manager sees that the play runs smoothly.

RI.3.2 Determine the main idea of a text; recount the key details and explain how they support the main idea.

Drama

Read the
full text

Drama

Read the passage.

Circle the name of Shakespeare's play.

Underline the sentence that tells us about the play's setting.

Color two sentences that describe what the play is about.

William Shakespeare wrote plays more than 300 years ago. One of his most famous plays is *Romeo and Juliet*.

The play is set in Italy. It is the story of a young man and woman who fall in love. Their families are enemies who don't want Romeo and Juliet to be together. The story has sword fighting, love, sadness, and humor.

There have been many interpretations of *Romeo and Juliet*. An interpretation is the way the play is presented. The story and words remain the same, but the setting changes.

The *Romeo and Juliet* story has been used in computer games, songs, operas, ballets, and more than 40 films.

Highlight the definition of *interpretation*.

Circle the part of a play that changes with different interpretations.

Underline the different ways in which the *Romeo and Juliet* story has been used.

1 What is the **key point** or **main idea** of the text?

_____

_____

2 List three **details** that support the main idea.

a _____

_____

b _____

_____

c _____

_____

RI.3.2 Determine the main idea of a text; recount the key details and explain how they support the main idea.

143

Compound words

Compound words are two or more words that are put together to make one word; e.g., bullfrog, suitcase.

List **1** **Write the word.**

teaspoon _____

seafood _____

sunrise _____

toothbrush _____

baseball _____

rainbow _____

footprint _____

moonlight _____

eyesight _____

homework _____

shoelace _____

earring _____

grandmother _____

fireworks _____

waterfall _____

butterfly _____

sunflower _____

airport _____

keyhole _____

afternoon _____

2 **Fill in the missing part.**

a tea_____

b moon_____

c tooth_____

d _____fall

e _____ball

f sun_____

g _____bow

h _____noon

i shoe_____

j sun_____

3 **Unscramble these words.**

a fsodeoa _____

b oprnoftit _____

c yseighte _____

d eworhmko _____

e wfirorkse _____

f uttrefylb _____

g irpatro _____

h hyelkoe _____

4 **Write the compound word correctly.**

a I like to go jogging in the afterwhere. _____

b The recipe said to add a teaprint of sugar to the batter. _____

c I watched a butterlight fly over the garden. _____

d My grandstorm always makes the best lasagne. _____

e How can I brush my teeth if I can't find my toothspoon? _____

f We had fish and fries at a seaflower restaurant. _____

L.3.2.F Use spelling patterns and generalizations in writing words.

Compound words

1 **Revise your spelling list from page 144.** Write the compound word that these pictures make.

a  +

_____

b  +

_____

c +

_____

d  +

_____

Challenge words

2 **Write the word.**

everyone   _____

somewhere   _____

newspaper   _____

grasshopper   _____

thunderstorm   _____

skateboard   _____

lifeguard   _____

wheelbarrow   _____

supermarket   _____

honeycomb   _____

3 **Word clues.** Which challenge word means?

a   a small cart   _____

b   a person who keeps you safe

_____

c   something made by bees

_____

d   an insect   _____

e   a large store   _____

f   a publication   _____

g   all of us   _____

4 **Hidden words.** Find the the challenge word hidden in these letters.

a   olehthunderstormhsauo   _____

b   yeuskateboardouash   _____

c   kjsghgrasshopperoihad   _____

Ownership for plural nouns

To make a **plural noun** show ownership, add an **apostrophe** (')
plus **s**. If the plural noun already **ends in s**, just **add an apostrophe**
('); e.g., the children**'s** playground; both girls' dresses.

1 **Circle and write the word that shows ownership.**

a   I found the book in the children's section.   _____

b   The houses' roofs were red, black, and green.   _____

c   They loaded the tourists' bags onto the bus.   _____

d   The acrobats' costumes sparkled under the lights.   _____

e   The monkeys' long tails help them swing from trees.   _____

f   The mice's squeaks were coming from the cupboard.   _____

g   She found the boys' blazers at the back of the classroom.   _____

2 **Fill in the words.**

the <u>squirrels'</u> tails

a   the _____ wings

b   the _____ collars

3 **Fill in the words.**

a   The yolks that belong to the eggs are the _____ yolks.

b   The kennels that belong to the dogs are the _____ kennels.

c   The scarves that belong to the women are the _____ scarves.

d   The tricks that belong to the magicians are the _____ tricks.

e   The teeth that belong to the crocodiles are the _____ teeth.

Spelling

Use this review to test your knowledge. It has three parts—**Spelling, Grammar,** and **Comprehension**. If you're unsure of an answer, go back and read the rules and generalizations in the blue boxes.

You have learned about:

- verb endings: ies, ied
- soft c and g
- suffixes: ful, less

- augh, ough
- irregular past tense verbs
- silent t, n, u

- suffix: ed
- endings: ery, ary, ory
- compound words

1 **The spelling mistakes in these sentences have been <u>underlined</u>. Write the correct spelling.** 2 marks

a Dad <u>wraped</u> our presents in spotted paper. _____

b I <u>spoted</u> a wren in the trees. _____

c We cooked <u>risse</u> to make sushi for dinner. _____

d Coach gave us <u>oranjes</u> at half-time. _____

2 **Write the compound word that matches the pictures.** 3 marks

a + = _____

b + = _____

c + = _____

d + = _____

3 **Which word correctly completes this sentence?** 1 mark

"But I wanted a pet frog for my birthday," _____ Ali.

a cried   b cryed   c crying   d cry

4 **Which word correctly completes this sentence?** 1 mark

I washed the dishes and Via _____ them.

a dry   b drys   c dried   d drying

5 **Each sentence has one word that is incorrect. Write the correct spelling.** 2 marks

a In Germany we saw many huge medieval casles. _____

b Last summer we sleeped under the stars. _____

c I writed a song about my Mom to sing on her birthday. _____

d The doughter could whistle almost as well as her mother. _____

6 **Which word is opposite in meaning to powerful?** 1 mark

a unpowerful   b dispowerful   c powering   d powerless

Your score

☐

10

Grammar

You have learned about:

- end punctuation
- adverbs of time
- adverbial phrases

- abstract nouns
- contractions
- adjectival phrases

- pronoun-antecedent agreement
- prepositions
- punctuating dialogue

1 **Fill in the end punctuation for each sentence.** 2 marks

a What is the capital city of the United States of America

b What a big dog that is

c The keys are on the kitchen table

d How will you solve this problem

2 **Fill in the abstract noun that matches the underlined adjective.** 2 marks

a Someone who is very <u>happy</u> is full of _____.

b Someone who is <u>healthy</u> has good _____.

c Someone who is <u>angry</u> is full of _____.

d Someone who is <u>wise</u> has great _____.

3 **Circle the pronoun that correctly completes each sentence.** 2 marks

a Joe is talking to Sadie and Dan because (he, they) are his friends.

b Annie will eat the pie when (she, it) finishes her chores.

c Felix picked up the book and put (him, it) in his bag.

d The children ran to their parents and told (they, them) the news.

4 **In each sentence, fill in the missing pronoun.** 2 marks

a The kind lady gave the man some food because _____ was hungry.

b Grandma baked the cookies and we ate _____.

5 **Circle the adverb in each sentence.** 2 marks

a I found out yesterday that I was getting an award.

b Our friends should be arriving soon.

c The newspaper comes out weekly.

d I often see my neighbor walking her dog.

Grammar

6 **Write the contraction for each group of words.** 3 marks

a does not _____

b will not _____

c we have _____

d cannot _____

e could have _____

f they will _____

7 **In each sentence, fill in the missing preposition.** 2 marks

a The stone sank to the bottom _____ the pool.

b The cat _____ the curly tail belongs to my friend.

c I am going _____ the beach with my friends.

d A tree sends its roots _____ the ground.

8 **In each sentence, state whether the underlined phrase is doing the work of an adjective or an adverb.** 2 marks

a I like to ride my bike <u>in the park</u>. _____

b The girl <u>in the blue dress</u> is my sister. _____

c My friend lives in the house <u>with the tall chimney</u>. _____

d I ran <u>around the track</u> six times. _____

9 **In the following sentences, fill in the missing punctuation.** 3 marks

a Ryan said I'm getting a bike for my birthday.

b I sat next to Marcia on the bus said Maria.

Your score

☐
___
20

Flight of the Falcon

Read the passage and then use the comprehension skills you have learned to answer the questions.

Geraldine Georgina Jones loved making models. Her room was filled with model ships, airplanes, birds, trains, and tiny animals. She had just finished painting Falcon on the biggest model plane she had ever made when disaster struck!

A sudden gust of wind swooped through the window. It lifted up the plane and sent it gliding around the room. The plane bumped against her giraffe, knocking it off the shelf. The giraffe hit the side of the tall ship. Both ended in splinters on the floor. Geraldine gaped at the mess.

But the wind had not finished its little game. It gathered up her tiny animals and sent them spinning around the room. Geraldine rushed to the window and slammed it shut. Without the wind to hold them up, the animals fell to the floor, and broke into even tinier pieces.

Geraldine sat on the floor amongst the broken bits and pieces. The plane glided gently down and landed beside her. She took one look at it and burst into tears.

1 What was Geraldine's hobby? 1 mark   LITERAL
- **a** flying paper planes
- **b** collecting models
- **c** making models
- **d** painting pictures

2 What is the most likely reason Geraldine called her model plane *Falcon*? 1 mark
Like a falcon, a plane …   CRITICAL
- **a** is silver.
- **b** makes short, high-pitched sounds.
- **c** can make its wings longer or shorter.
- **d** can fly fast.

Flight of the Falcon

3 Which material did Geraldine use to make the giraffe and the ship? 1 mark   **INFERENTIAL**

a   wood   b   paper

c   metal   d   cardboard

4 What was the main cause of the disaster in Geraldine's room? 1 mark   **INFERENTIAL**

a   the model plane   b   the wind

c   the T-Rex   d   the tall ship

5 Give a text clue to support your answer to question 4.   2 marks   **CRITICAL**

_____

_____

_____

6 What happened when Geraldine shut the window? 1 mark   **INFERENTIAL**

a   The tiny animals fell and broke.   b   The plane landed on the floor.

c   The tiny animals lifted off the shelf. d   Geraldine sat on the floor.

7 Geraldine gaped at the mess. This means ... 1 marks   **VOCABULARY**

a   she took a quick look.   b   she stared with her mouth open.

c   she giggled.   d   she stepped backwards.

8 Why do you think Geraldine burst into tears? 2 marks   **CRITICAL**

_____

_____

_____

Your
score

☐
10

Your Review 3 Scores

Spelling		Grammar		Comprehension		Total
☐	+	☐	+	☐	=	☐
10		**20**		**10**		**40**

The Illawarry Cassary

Cause and effect
To find cause and effect, ask why something happens and what the result is.

Read the passage.

Put a box around what the narrator did to pretend he was bored.

Highlight the sentence that shows why the narrator almost choked.

Color the clue to why the narrator called himself an idiot.

Underline what the narrator said when Angus asked to see the bird.

"I've got an illawarry cassary," I said.

Angus eyeballed me. "A what?"

"An illawarry cassary. It's a type of meat-eating bird."

"How come," said Angus, still standing with his elbows across his chest, "we haven't heard about this bird before?"

"You never asked," I said, and yawned as if I was really bored.

"We'd like to see it."

I almost choked in mid-yawn. "You idiot!" I was thinking. Of course they'd want to see it. I thought fast. "It always spits on strangers."

Circle the correct answer for each question.

1 What **happened** when Angus asked why they'd never heard of the narrator's bird before? The narrator pretended to be ...

   a confused.   **b** upset.   **c** surprised.   **d** bored.

2 What **caused** the narrator to almost choke?

   a gulping in too much air   **b** shock when he heard what Angus said

   c a tickle in his throat   **d** excitement when he heard what Angus said

3 **Why** did the narrator call himself an idiot?

   a He'd spoken without thinking.   **b** He should have brought the bird with him.

   c He was embarrassed about choking.   **d** He should have chosen a different pet.

4 What is the most likely **reason** the narrator said his bird spat on strangers?

   a to impress Angus   **b** to encourage Angus to come and see it

   c to stop Angus wanting to see it   **d** to warn Angus not to get too close to it

The Illawarry Cassary

Read the whole story
The Illawarry Cassary

Read the passage.

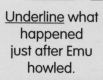
<u>Underline</u> what happened just after Emu howled.

Color why the narrator was surprised when the boys ran away.

Emu gave another howl. In less than a second, I heard three sets of feet running down the driveway.

I couldn't move. What was going on? Surely they weren't scared of a little wet bantam calling out for his dinner? Hadn't they ever seen a chicken before? I stepped forward to go and get Emu in out of the rain, when I suddenly saw it. From where Angus, Martin, and Alex had stood, Emu was a two-meter-tall, spiky-feathered, war-helmeted, bloodcurdle-screaming, hungry, illawarry cassary!

At school these days we never talk about our pets. And no-one calls me Flake anymore!

Highlight the reason Angus, Martin and Alex ran away.

<u>Underline</u> two things that are different at school these days.

1. What **happened** just after Emu howled? _____

_____

2. **Why** was the narrator surprised that Angus, Martin, and Alex were running away?

_____

_____

3. What had **caused** Angus, Martin, and Alex to run away?

_____

_____

4. Name two things that **happened as a result** of the boys seeing the narrator's 'illawarry cassary.'

_____

_____

squ, sch, sph

The letters **qu** make the single sound **kw**.
Many words start with **squ**; e.g., **squ**eak.
The letters **ch** can make the single sounds.
Some words start with **sch**; e.g., **sch**eme.
The letters **ph** make the single sound **f**.
Some words start with **sph**; e.g., **sph**ere.

List ① Write the word.

squad _____

squat _____

squid _____

squint _____

school _____

sphere _____

square _____

squish _____

squeal _____

squash _____

squirt _____

squiggle _____

sphinx _____

scheme _____

squirrel _____

squeeze _____

squelch _____

squeaky _____

squirm _____

squall _____

② Sort the words.

Words with *squ*

_____ _____

_____ _____

_____ _____

_____ _____

_____ _____

_____ _____

_____ _____

_____ _____

Words with *sch*

_____ _____

Words with *sph*

_____ _____

③ Unscramble these words.

a eeezqus _____ **b** suatq _____

c rrelqusi _____ **d** qusare _____

e oolchs _____ **f** queaksy _____

g unitsq _____ **h** elchqus _____

i qusad _____ **j** gugliqse _____

④ Name.

a _____ **b** _____ **c** _____ **d** _____

L.3.2.F Use spelling patterns and generalizations in writing words.

squ, sch, sph

1 **Revise your spelling list from page 154.** Underline the mistake.
Write the word correctly.

a My new water gun can squert water at someone yards away. _____

b When I blew the whistle, it made a skweaky sound. _____

c I had to sqweeze the ketchup out of the bottle. _____

d I tried to sqwish the bug with my shoe. _____

e The girl's piercing sqweal hurt everyone's ears. _____

f I tried to sqwash as many clothes as possible into my suitcase. _____

g A police sqwad arrived quickly at the crime scene. _____

h The sun's light was so bright it made me sqwint. _____

Challenge words

2 **Write the word.**

squawk _____

scholar _____

squabble _____

squadron _____

squeamish _____

squatter _____

squelchy _____

spherical _____

atmosphere _____

hemisphere _____

3 **Hidden words.** Find the challenge word.

a ncassquabbleioyd _____

b loatmospherejshu _____

c sdfgsquawkcasoh _____

d aloesquadronobsaj _____

e asdhusphericalfgua _____

f uianlsquatteroiadh _____

4 **Complete the sentence.**

a The United States of America is in the
northern _____.

b The ball was _____ in shape.

c The Air Force _____ trained hard.

5 **Word clues.** Which challenge word means?

a made sick by unpleasant sights _____

b a half of any sphere _____

c the gases surrounding planets _____

d a squishing or sucking sound _____

Comparative adjectives

Adjectives can be used to **compare** two or more people or things with each other. They end in **er** or **est**, or they have **more** or **most** in front of them; e.g., **taller**, **tallest**, **more** comfortable, **most** comfortable.

1 **Fill in the words.** cutest cuter funnier funniest

a All three chimps are funny, but the little one is the _____.

b The clown with the red nose is _____ than the one wearing the purple hat.

c All of the kittens are cute, but the black one is the _____.

d This little kitten is much _____ than that one.

2 **Sort the words.**

Comparing two		**Comparing more than two**
_____	more obedient	_____
_____	scariest weakest	_____
_____	angriest happier	_____
_____	most anxious	_____
_____	more pleased	_____
_____	loosest younger	_____
	cuddlier worst	
	better	

3 **Circle the adjectives that compare.**

a Of all the seasons, winter is the coldest.

b The elephant is the largest animal on land.

c We traveled on the straighter of the two roads.

d That is the most interesting book I have ever read.

e These oranges are sweeter than the ones we bought last week.

Lookout London

Making inferences
To make inferences while reading, use clues in the text. The clues help you find the answers that are hiding in the text.

Read the passage.

Circle where the parcel was.

Underline how long it will take to get to London.

Highlight why Charles E. Worthington needs help.

Color two things the wristbands can do.

Hello Will and Vika. You are needed urgently in London, England. Charles E. Worthington needs your help. Something very important is missing. Do not delay. In the corner of the room, under this junk, you will find a parcel containing two transporter wristbands. You must wear these wristbands at all times. They allow you to travel at the blink of an eye and they will keep us in contact.

Remember, this mission is Top Secret. Do not tell anyone you are SWAT agents. You must leave at once.

Circle the correct answer for each question.

1 Which is the best **inference**? Will and Vika are in a ...

   a neat room.   **b** grand room.   **c** big room.   **d** messy room.

2 Which word is the **clue** to question 1's answer?

   a parcel   **b** junk   **c** important   **d** corner

3 How long will it take Will and Vika to get to London?

   a hours   **b** weeks   **c** days   **d** seconds

4 Which phrase is the **clue** to number 3's answer?

   a the blink of an eye   **b** Do not delay

   c at all times   **d** allow you to travel

5 What is the most likely reason Charles E. Worthington needs Will and Vika's help?

   a to find out what's missing   **b** to find what's missing

   c to learn about being a SWAT agent   **d** to find a parcel

RL.3.1 Ask and answer questions to demonstrate understanding of a text, referring explicitly to the text as the basis for the answers.

Lookout London

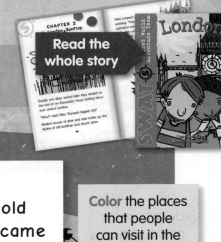

Read the whole story

Read the passage.

Underline Charlie's description of the West End.

Circle the word that means *lots of activity and movement.*

Color the places that people can visit in the West End.

Once across the park they took a shortcut through some of London's old and narrow cobbled laneways. They came out at Piccadilly Circus.

"This part of the West End is the world's theater capital," said Charlie.

There were signs everywhere saying what was on, what was coming, and who was starring. It was a bustle of restaurants, cafes, theaters, and cinemas. The three of them walked over to a half-price ticket booth. The lady recognized Charlie straight away.

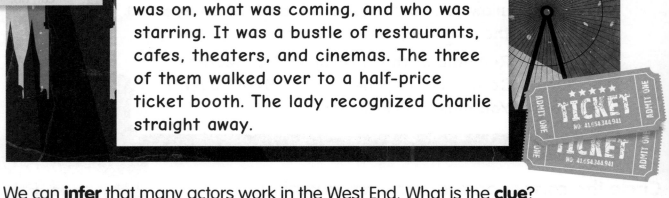

1. We can **infer** that many actors work in the West End. What is the **clue**?

_____

_____

_____

2. What does the word *bustle* **suggest** about the kind of place the West End is?

_____

_____

_____

3. What does the passage **suggest** about the kinds of things people can do in the West End?

_____

_____

_____

RL.3.1 Ask and answer questions to demonstrate understanding of a text, referring explicitly to the text as the basis for the answers.

Suffix: y

> Adding the suffix **y** to a noun or verb turns it into an adjective; e.g., health → healt**hy**.
>
> If the noun or verb ends in a consonant with a <u>short vowel before</u> it, **double the consonant** before adding **y**; e.g., chop ch**oppy**.
>
> When the verb or noun ends in **e**, drop the **e** before adding **y**; e.g., sparkl**e** → sparkl**y**.

List ① **Write the word.**

windy _____

sleepy _____

cloudy _____

rainy _____

tricky _____

dusty _____

creamy _____

fatty _____

muddy _____

easy _____

funny _____

watery _____

stormy _____

thirsty _____

floppy _____

shiny _____

smoky _____

greasy _____

snappy _____

scary _____

② **Unravel these list words.**

a oludcy _____

b nynuf _____

c lpopyf _____

d tomrsy _____

e lsypee _____

③ **Missing letters.** Write the missing letters.

a cr ___ ___ m ___   b gr ___ ___ s ___

c wa ___ ___ ___ y   d ___ ___ ___ ty

e ___ ___ ___ ___ py   f th ___ ___ st ___

④ **Meaning.** Which list word means?

a Causing laughter or amusement

_____

b Hanging or flapping in a loose way

_____

c Feeling a need to drink _____

d Quick, rapid or sudden _____

⑤ **Word clue.** Which list word means?

a like or looking like smoke _____

b covered in dust or powder _____

c frightening _____

d a great amount of wind _____

e covered in mud _____

f rain, wind, thunder, and lightning _____

L.3.2.F Use spelling patterns and generalizations in writing words.

159

Suffix: y

1 **Revise your spelling list from page 159.** Underline the mistake.
Write the word correctly.

a On windie days, we like to fly our kites.   _____

b On dark and stormi nights, I like to cuddle up in bed.   _____

c After the rain, our backyard was all mudie.   _____

d My sister likes to watch scari movies.   _____

e The kitchen was smookey when Dad burned the toast.   _____

f Our homemade ice cream was soft and creemy.   _____

g It was a cold and clowdy day.   _____

h I stayed up late, so I felt quite slepi in the morning.   _____

Challenge words

2 **Write the word.**

healthy   _____

sparkly   _____

breezy   _____

noisy   _____

squeaky   _____

drowsy   _____

woolly   _____

spongy   _____

spicy   _____

prickly   _____

3 **Complete the sentence.**

a The _____ meal made her mouth burn.

b The sea looked _____ in the sunshine.

c The sheep was white and _____.

d The door made a _____ sound when it opened.

e Salad is a _____ meal.

f The cactus had _____ spikes.

g The ground was _____ close to the lake.

4 **Another way to say it.** Which challenge word could replace the underlined word?

a The weather was <u>windy</u> and cool.   _____

b The mattress was <u>springy</u> and comfortable.   _____

c The dog's bark was <u>loud</u>.   _____

d He felt <u>sleepy</u> after eating the large meal.   _____

L.3.2.F Use spelling patterns and generalizations in writing words.

Comparative adverbs

Adverbs can compare **how** or **when** something happens or is done; e.g., The Smiths arrived **earlier** than the Delgados. Sometimes the **comparison** is shown by placing more, most, less, or least before the **adverb**; e.g., She sang **most beautifully** of all.

1 **Circle the adverb that correctly completes each sentence.**

a   Felix can run (fast, faster, fastest) than Jasper.

b   Of the three girls, Ellie threw her ball the (far, farther, farthest).

c   Some stars sparkle (brightly, less brightly, least brightly) than others.

d   I am feeling (bad, worse, worst) than I did this morning.

e   Ruby works (hard, harder, hardest) than her brother.

f   The (soon, sooner, soonest) they can get here is 12 o'clock.

g   Cameron jumped (high, higher, highest) of all the competitors.

2 **Color the adverb in each sentence.**

a   He greeted me more politely the second time.

b   She writes more neatly than her sister.

c   The buses run more frequently than the trains.

d   I see her less often than I used to.

e   The girls are more warmly dressed than the boys.

f   Of all the students, Fran speaks the most clearly.

g   The doctor told me to eat more healthily.

3 **Complete the table.**

Adverb	Comparing two	Comparing more than two
carefully	more carefully	most carefully
	more proudly	
		most gracefully
calmly		
	more recently	

L.3.1.A Explain the function of adverbs in general and their functions in particular sentences.

161

Hedgehogs in the City

Making connections
Linking a text to events in your own life is a great way to build understanding. Look for key words and phrases in the text to make the connections.

Read the passage.

In paragraph 1, (circle) one verb that describes something you have done or might do.

In paragraph 2, **highlight** something you have thrown or might throw in the garbage bin.

In paragraph 3, underline what might happen if you dropped a glass jar.

In paragraph 3, **color** what the sand felt like.

Zed and DD, each wrapped in a pickle jar, tipped over, and began to roll slowly. The bottled hedgehogs picked up speed, bumping and spinning their way down Garbage Hill.

They skipped over old cars and spun off slimy piles of vegetables, getting air as they hurtled forever downwards.

The two jars collided in midair before landing with a PLUNK! DD's jar smashed into a million pieces. Zed's jar spun on the spot until he popped out, fast as a cork. He shot along the sand, grinding his way to a gritty stop.

Circle the correct answers.

1 Which of the following have you done, or might you do?

a buy a jar of pickles

b throw an empty pickle jar in the garbage truck

c roll down a slope in a pickle jar

d store things in an empty pickle jar

e roll down a slope

f see a hedgehog

g see a hedgehog in a pickle jar

h play on a trash heap

i collide with someone

j watch an empty pickle jar smash into pieces

k fall in the sand

l collide with someone while wrapped in a pickle jar

Hedgehogs in the City

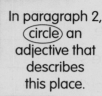

Read the
whole story

Hedgehogs
in The City

by Ned Pike and Freya Pike
illustrated by Luke Junevicius

Read the passage.

Underline the reason this place reminds the hedgehogs of home.

The three hedgehogs fell into an oasis: a place that only a hedgehog could dream of. Piles of rotting trash filled the air with sweet aromas. It smelled like home.

As the hedgehogs settled on top of the heap, they slowly took in the landscape. Animals of all kinds stared back at them. This was a magical place where all animals were equal and humans did most of the work. "This really is paradise," Ruttel mused.

In paragraph 2, circle an adjective that describes this place.

Highlight the key words that tell us who lives in this place.

Color the word Ruttel uses to describe this place.

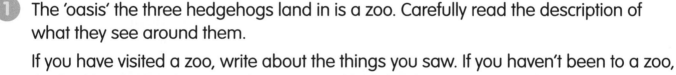

1 The 'oasis' the three hedgehogs land in is a zoo. Carefully read the description of what they see around them.

If you have visited a zoo, write about the things you saw. If you haven't been to a zoo, think of books you have read and write about the things you would expect to see.

_____

_____

_____

_____

_____

_____

_____

_____

_____

RL.3.1 Ask and answer questions to demonstrate understanding of a text, referring explicitly to the text as the basis for the answers.

163

Contractions

> When two words join to make a shorter word, it is called a **contraction**. The words are shortened by leaving out letters, which are replaced by an apostrophe ('); e.g., you will → you'll.

List ① **Write the word.**

I'm _____

I'll _____

I've _____

she's _____

they'll _____

what's _____

it's _____

we'll _____

we've _____

that's _____

isn't _____

can't _____

hasn't _____

won't _____

didn't _____

don't _____

who's _____

we're _____

they're _____

o'clock _____

② **Write the matching contraction.**

a cannot _____

b they will _____

c what is _____

d they are _____

e we have _____

f I will _____

g do not _____

h I have _____

i it is _____

j will not _____

③ **Rewrite the word with the apostrophe.**

a Im _____ b theyll _____

c dont _____ d Ill _____

e oclock _____ f whos _____

g hasnt _____ h theyre _____

i weve _____ j didnt _____

k thats _____ l wont _____

m shes _____ n were _____

④ **Correct contraction.** Circle the correct contraction.

a	what is	what's / wha'ts	b	is not	isn't / isnt'	c	cannot	ca'nt / can't
d	we are	w'ere / we're	e	I have	Iv'e / I've	f	she is	she's / sh'es
g	it is	it's / i'ts	h	we will	we'll / w'ell	i	that is	tha'ts / that's

L.3.2 Demonstrate command of the conventions of punctuation when writing.

Contractions

1 **Revise your spelling list from page 164.** Underline the mistake.
Write the word correctly.

a   Im' going to my room.   _____

b   Is'nt it hot today!   _____

c   I was so tired I did'nt want to get out of bed.   _____

d   You should'nt say nasty things about your friends.   _____

e   Wev'e decided to go bowling tomorrow.   _____

f   We will meet at 1 oclo'ck under the big oak tree.   _____

g   Do'nt tell me what to do!   _____

h   W'ere going to the zoo tomorrow.   _____

Challenge words

2 **Write the word.**

aren't   _____

must've   _____

doesn't   _____

couldn't   _____

wouldn't   _____

shouldn't   _____

would've   _____

could've   _____

should've   _____

might've   _____

3 **Complete the sentence.**

a   Sadly, she _____ come as
she was on vacation.

b   They _____ be playing on
the broken equipment.

c   He _____ reach the top
shelf as he was too short.

d   It _____ matter when you
get here as long as it's today.

e   I _____ helped her if I
could've.

f   We _____ going away until
next week.

4 **Another way to say it.** Which challenge word could replace the underlined words?

a   We <u>must have</u> missed each other by a few minutes.   _____

b   They <u>could have</u> eaten all the pizza, but they saved me a piece.   _____

c   You <u>should not</u> run around the swimming pool.   _____

d   She <u>should have</u> come to the party with you.   _____

Quotation marks in direct speech

We use **quotation marks** (" ") to show what someone says in direct speech. They go around the exact words the person says, including any punctuation; e.g., **"I like chocolate ice cream,"** said Ben.

1 **Underline the exact words the people say in these sentences.**

  a   "Where did you buy those red shoes?" asked Milly.

  b   "The neighbors have bought a new car," said Tim.

  c   "Look at that beautiful building!" exclaimed the tourist.

  d   Mom announced, "We are going to the zoo next week."

  e   Omar said, "My favorite animals are elephants and giraffes."

  f   "I asked him a question," said Connor, "but he didn't answer me."

  g   "Finish your chores first," said Dad, "and then you can go and play."

2 **Fill in the quotation marks.**

  a   Are you coming to my party on Saturday? asked Lily.

  b   I got lots of presents for my birthday, said Lucas.

  c   Can I watch TV when I've finished my violin practice? asked Sam.

  d   Dylan said, I have lots of aunts, uncles, and cousins.

  e   Do all lions have big, bushy manes? asked the little boy.

  f   I've spent hours reading the book, said Myra, and I still haven't finished it.

  g   Would you like a chocolate milkshake? asked Kai. Or would you rather have a chocolate ice cream?

3 **Cross out the quotation marks that aren't needed.**

  a   "Do you like apple pie?" asked Myrna."

  b   "I love it," said Laurie," "and I also like choc chip cookies."

Why Bear Has a Stumpy Tail

Sequencing events
To identify the sequence of events in a text, look at words that give clues to the order in which things happen.

Read the passage.

<u>Underline</u> the event that happened first.

Highlight the first thing Fox said Bear should do.

Color what should happen just before Bear gives his tail a strong tug.

Fox saw her friend, Bear. Fox had just stolen a string of fish.

"Can you share them with me?" asked Bear.

"No!" snapped Fox. "Catch your own."

"How can I?" asked Bear. "The lake is frozen."

"Cut a hole in the ice," said Fox. "Then, stick your tail in the lake and hold it there as long as you can. It will hurt when the fish grab it. When you think you have enough fish, give your tail a strong tug to pull out the fish."

1 Which event happened first in the text? Circle the correct answer.

   a Fox saw her friend Bear.   b Fox stole some fish.

2 Number the actions to show the order in which they should happen.

  ☐ Fox said that Bear should wait until his tail started to hurt.

  ☐ Fox said that Bear should cut a hole in the ice.

  ☐ Fox said that Bear should pull out the fish.

  ☐ Fox said that Bear should stick his tail in the water.

Why Bear Has a Stumpy Tail

Read the passage.

Underline what Bear did while Fox watched on.

Highlight the words that show when Bear started pulling at his tail.

Fox watched as Bear put his tail in the water. Then she ran off laughing. Bear thought he felt some fish bite his tail. But what he was really feeling was water freezing around his tail. When the pain got too great, he pulled at his tail. Nothing happened. He pulled harder. He pulled so hard that his tail broke off. All that was left was a little stumpy tail, like bears have today.

Circle the time word in the second sentence.

Color the sentence that shows what happened when Bear pulled his tail out of the water.

1 **When** did Fox leave? _____

_____

_____

2 **When** did the water start freezing around Bear's tail? _____

_____

_____

3 **When** did Bear start pulling at his tail? _____

_____

_____

4 What **finally** happened to Bear's tail? _____

_____

_____

RL.3.1 Ask and answer questions to demonstrate understanding of a text, referring explicitly to the text as the basis for the answers.

Irregular plurals

> Some nouns become plural by changing in other ways, or not changing at all; e.g., 1 child → 2 children, 1 fish → 2 fish.
>
> To change some singular nouns that end in **f** or **fe** into plurals, change the **f** or **fe** to **v** before adding **es**; e.g., 1 thie**f** → 2 thie**ves**.

List **1** **Write the word.**

leaves _____

roofs _____

men _____

mice _____

sheep _____

lives _____

cliffs _____

wolves _____

children _____

music _____

loaves _____

chiefs _____

geese _____

people _____

bread _____

calves _____

chefs _____

women _____

trousers _____

scarves _____

2 **Make the words plural.**

a woman _____

b scarf _____

c mouse _____

d calf _____

e man _____

f bread _____

g life _____

h leaf _____

i chief _____

j person _____

3 **Complete these words with *ves* or *fs*.**

a loa_____

b roo_____

c che_____

d clif_____

e cal_____

f wol_____

g lea_____

4 **Name.**

a _____   b _____   c _____   d _____

Irregular plurals

1 **Revise your spelling list from page 169.** Underline the mistake. Write the word correctly.

a I have two pet mouses. _____

b The sheeps are in the meadow. _____

c The gooses hissed at us. _____

d The mans are over there. _____

e There were lots of peoples at Disneyland. _____

f We bought two loaves of breads. _____

g The womans are setting out the food. _____

h The childs are playing outside. _____

Challenge words

2 **Write the word.**

knives _____

shelves _____

beliefs _____

oases _____

cacti _____

thieves _____

ellipses _____

equipment _____

furniture _____

spectacles _____

3 **Complete the sentence.**

a The _____ stole the expensive jewel.

b My grandmother can't see as she has lost her _____ .

c The _____ were all different colors, but they were all prickly.

d They bought new _____ to go on the back porch.

e Her _____ were filled with books.

f He had strong _____ about animal rights.

4 **Word clues.** Which list word means?

a areas in a desert where plants grow _____

b punctuation using three dots _____

c tools with sharp, thin blades _____

d things used for particular activities _____

L.3.2.F Use spelling patterns and generalizations in writing words.

Saying, thinking, and feeling verbs

Saying verbs are a type of **action verb**. They tell us what someone says; e.g., *He told her where to go.* **Thinking and feeling verbs** show what is going on in our heads; e.g., *I understand the problem. I want more ice cream.*

1 **Fill in the gaps with a verb from the box.**

a "What is that?" _____ Jarred.

b Zoe _____ how to spell the words.

c Simon _____ a bicycle for his birthday.

d "Watch out!" _____ Mr. Rivera.

e They _____ we should have more rules.

f The children _____ seeing the animals.

g He _____ all the students' questions.

> wants
> think
> knows
> answered
> asked
> enjoyed
> yelled

2 **Sort the words.**

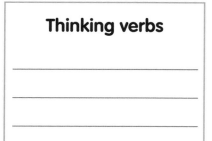

| thought | wished | replied | guessed | loved |
| announced | shouted | hated | remembered |

Saying verbs	**Thinking verbs**	**Feeling verbs**
_____	_____	_____
_____	_____	_____
_____	_____	_____

3 **Circle the saying verbs and underline the thinking verbs in the following sentences.**

a He shouted at the boy.

b She believes she is right.

c They guessed the answers.

d We said they could help us.

e I suppose that's alright.

f I wonder whose book this is.

L.3.1.A Explain the function of verbs in general and their functions in particular sentences.

171

Limericks

Visualization
Visualizing pictures of the people, places, things, and events you are reading about helps build better understanding of the text. Looking for key words in the text will help you create the images.

Read the passage.

Circle the adjective that describes the lady.

Highlight the phrase that describes what the lady's chin looked like.

Color the instrument the lady played.

Circle the adjective that describes the man.

Underline the adjective that describes the man's nose.

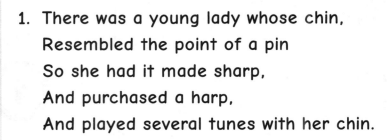

1. There was a young lady whose chin,
   Resembled the point of a pin
   So she had it made sharp,
   And purchased a harp,
   And played several tunes with her chin.

2. There was an old man with a nose,
   Who said, "If you choose to suppose
   That my nose is too long,
   you are certainly wrong!"
   That remarkable man with a nose.

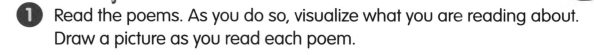

1 Read the poems. As you do so, visualize what you are reading about. Draw a picture as you read each poem.

Poem 1	Poem 2

Limericks

Read the passage.

Circle the word that helped you see what the old man looked like.

Put a box around the word that helped you see what the young lady wore on her head.

1. There was an old man with a beard,
   Who said, "It is just as I feared!
   Two owls and a hen,
   Four larks and a wren,
   Have all built their nests in my beard!"

2. There was a young lady whose bonnet,
   Came untied when the birds sat upon it;
   But she said: "I don't care!
   All the birds in the air
   Are welcome to sit on my bonnet!"

Highlight the words that helped you see the different birds.

Underline the words that helped you see how the lady's bonnet came untied.

1 Read the poems again. As you do so, visualize what you are reading about. Draw a picture as you read each poem.

Poem 1	Poem 2

Suffix: ly

Adding the suffix **ly** to an adjective turns it into an adverb; eg., quick → quick**ly**.

If the adjextive ends in **y**, change the **y** to **i** before adding **ly**; e.g, happy → happ**i**ly.

List ① **Write the word.**

sadly _____
slowly _____
quickly _____
suddenly _____
closely _____
strongly _____
surely _____
happily _____
hopefully _____
exactly _____
carefully _____
extremely _____
easily _____
luckily _____
heavily _____
angrily _____
busily _____
properly _____
perfectly _____
nervously _____

② **Fill in the missing letters.**

a s ___ r ___ ng ___ ___
b ___ ur ___ l ___
c ca ___ ef ___ ___ ___ ___
d e ___ s ___ l ___
e ___ uck ___ ___ ___
f an ___ ___ i ___ ___
g sl ___ ___ l ___
h b ___ ___ ___ ly
i ne ___ ___ ___ ___ sly
j q ___ i ___ k ___ y
k su ___ ___ ___ n ___ y

③ **In a group.** Write the list word that belongs in each group.

a angry, angrier, _____
b easy, easier, _____
c close, closer, _____
d quick, quicker, _____
e happy, happier, _____
f hope, hopeful, _____

④ **Meaning.** Which list word means?

a Fortunately _____
b Unhappily _____
c Without fault or mistake _____
d With great movement, force, or energy _____
e In a cautious manner _____
f In a correct or accurate way _____

Suffix: ly

1 **Revise your spelling list from page 174.** Write the word in parentheses correctly.

a (Hopeful) _____ I'll be able to play next week.

b (Sad) _____ my oldest friend is moving away tomorrow.

c We used a magnifying glass to look (close) _____ at the insect.

d (Lucky) _____ I brought my umbrella with me as it's started raining.

e The doctor (careful) _____ removed the patient's bandages.

f He sat down (heavy) _____ and broke the chair.

g I left my brother and sister playing (happy) _____ in the corner.

h I practiced and practiced until I could play the song (perfect) _____.

Challenge words

2 **Write the word.**

noisily _____

steadily _____

certainly _____

wearily _____

regularly _____

fortunately _____

anxiously _____

definitely _____

immediately _____

successfully _____

3 **Hidden words.** Find the challenge word.

a seffortunatelyasih _____

b mimmediatelyiy _____

c ysbjanoisilysado _____

d mpqzlcertainlynsof _____

e lawivregularlyoinsc _____

4 **Word clues.** Which challenge word means?

a without any doubt _____

b routinely _____

c right away _____

d loudly _____

5 **Complete with a challenge word.**

a A word that means the same as now is _____.

b A word that means the opposite of unlucky is _____.

c A word that shows you do something often is _____.

d A word that shows you're worried about something is _____.

L.3.2.E Use conventional spelling for high-frequency and other studied words and for adding suffixes to base words.

175

Punctuating sentences

Punctuation helps readers understand writing.

Periods (.), question marks (?) and exclamation points (!) end sentences; e.g., My name is Kim. What is your name? What a great name!

Commas (,) separate parts of a sentence and items in a list; e.g., Although he's a small boy, he is very strong. Today I traveled on a bus, a train, and a ferry.

1 **Fill in a period, question mark, or exclamation point at the end of each sentence.**

a   When are you going to finish your project

b   What an adventure that was

c   The last time I went on a boat, I was seasick

d   When I'm overseas, I'll email you every day

e   What is the matter with your cat

f   How amazing was that ride

2 **Fill in the commas in these sentences.**

a   I have pens pencils highlighters and an eraser in my pencil case.

b   Although I like vanilla ice cream chocolate ice cream is my favorite.

c   She decorated the room with balloons streamers and fresh flowers.

d   If you're feeling tired you should rest for a while.

e   I've tried calling her but she doesn't answer her phone.

f   I saw puppies kittens fish mice and rabbits at the pet shop.

g   If you must know I've been to America Europe and Asia.

h   By the way those packets boxes and tins belong to me.

L.3.2.E Use conventional spelling for high-frequency and other studied words and for adding suffixes to base words.

Plants That Bite Back

Finding the main idea and supporting details
To discover what a text is about, look for the main idea or key point. Facts and details in the text can help you find the main idea.

Read the passage.

Color why insects are attracted to the plant.

Circle what causes the insect to stick to the plant.

Each leaf of the sundew plant has hundreds of tentacles. Each tentacle has a drop of sticky liquid on the end. When insects come to drink the nectar, they stick to the liquid. As an insect struggles to get free, the sticky tentacles wrap around its body. Now the plant begins to eat the insect's juicy flesh.

Underline what happens when the insect tries to free itself.

Highlight what finally happens to the insect.

Circle the correct answer/s for each question.

1 What is the **key point** or **main idea** of the text?

   a   to describe what a sundew looks like

   b   to explain how the sundew traps insects

   c   to explain why insects drink nectar

   d   to show how plants get their food

2 Which three details best **support** the main idea?

   a   The sundew has hundreds of tentacles.

   b   There is sticky liquid on the ends of the tentacles.

   c   An insect comes to drink the nectar.

   d   The insect sticks to the liquid.

   e   The insect struggles to get free.

   f   The sticky tentacles wrap around the insect's body.

   g   The sundew eats the insect.

Plants That Bite Back

Read the full text

Read the passage.

Underline how long a giraffe spends eating from a tree.

Highlight what happens when the giraffe starts to eat the leaves.

Color how long it takes before the leaves become too poisonous to eat.

The giraffes don't eat from one tree for very long. They munch away at a tree for a short time and then they move on.

People watching may think the giraffe is being nice to the tree. The real reason turns out to be very different.

The acacia tree has another way to defend itself—**poison**.

As the giraffe starts to munch on the spiky tree, the tree pushes poison into its leaves. Within 30 minutes the leaves are too poisonous to eat.

Circle the key word that tells us how the acacia tree protects itself from animals that want to eat its leaves.

1. What is the **key point** or **main idea** of the text?

_____

_____

_____

2. Which three **details** support the main idea?

a _____

_____

b _____

_____

c _____

_____

RI.3.2 Determine the main idea of a text; recount the key details and explain how they support the main idea.

Trigraph: ear

The letters **ear** make the single sound **ear**; e.g., f**ear**.

The letters **ear** can also make the single sound **air**; e.g., p**ear**.

Sometimes they make different sounds; e.g., **ear**ly, h**ear**t, **ear**th.

List **1** **Write the word.**

ear _____

near _____

bear _____

fear _____

wear _____

hear _____

pear _____

year _____

dear _____

gear _____

shear _____

earn _____

clear _____

Earth _____

learn _____

swear _____

smear _____

spear _____

yearly _____

heart _____

2 **Word clues.** Which list word means?

a   a body part you hear with _____

b   listen _____

c   365 days _____

d   our planet _____

e   a long wooden stick with a sharp point

_____

3 **Unscramble these words.**

a   frae _____   b   yrae _____

c   aerw _____   d   rean _____

e   aher _____   f   rae _____

g   raed _____   h   yyealr _____

i   rgea _____   j   earnl _____

k   heasr _____   l   arews _____

m   caerl _____   n   aerms _____

o   raep _____   p   thaer _____

q   raeps _____   r   raeb _____

s   rane _____   t   htrae _____

4 **Meaning.** Which list word means?

a   An organ that pumps blood _____

b   Not blocked, open _____

c   A machine part that helps it work _____

d   To spread on or over a surface _____

e   To get money _____

f   A sweet, bell-shaped fruit _____

Trigraph: ear

1 **Revise your spelling list from page 179.** Fill in the missing word.

a The hunter threw his _____ but it missed its target.

b I like to sit _____ the window to get some fresh air.

c The hikers stood still as a huge grizzly _____ walked past them.

d She whispered her secret in my _____.

e Venus is the closest planet to _____.

f This summer I am going to _____ how to play baseball.

g I grabbed an apple and a _____ from the fruit bowl.

h He has a _____ of large spiders.

Challenge words

2 **Write the word.**

beard _____

earring _____

pearl _____

dreary _____

heard _____

weary _____

nearby _____

appear _____

hearth _____

search _____

3 **Word clues.** Which challenge word means?

a tired _____

b smooth, round gem _____

c listened _____

d jewelry worn in the ear _____

e the floor of a fireplace _____

f not far away _____

g the hair on a man's face _____

h to become visible _____

i to look for something _____

j gloomy or dull _____

4 **Another way to say it.** Which challenge word could replace the underlined word?

a The man shaved his <u>stubble</u> off as it was itchy. _____

b The pirates went on a <u>hunt</u> for the buried treasure. _____

c The owners of the <u>neighboring</u> house were very friendly. _____

d We stayed indoors on the gray, <u>bleak</u> day. _____

L.3.2.F Use spelling patterns and generalizations in writing words.

Simple sentences

A sentence is a group of words that makes complete sense. A simple sentence has **one subject** and **one verb**; e.g., The **girl** **jumps** over the rope.

1 **Complete each sentence with a verb from the list.**

| have finished | have flown | has been stalking | are galloping | has fed |

a All the birds _____ away.

b The farmer _____ all the animals.

c The gardeners _____ all their work.

d The horses _____ around the meadow.

e The tiger _____ its prey.

2 **Find the subjects for these sentences in the box.**

a _____ lived millions of years ago.

b _____ slither along the ground.

c _____ travel on trains and buses.

d _____ serve food to customers.

e _____ perform in films and on stage.

Passengers

Actors

Woolly mammoths

Restaurants

Snakes

3 **Color the subjects in these proverbs.**

a Practice makes perfect.

b The early bird catches the worm.

c Every dog has his day.

d The walls have ears.

e Too many cooks spoil the broth.

f A cat has nine lives.

g A picture paints a thousand words.

h All cats are gray in the dark.

i A new broom sweeps clean.

j Pride comes before a fall.

Mountains

Read the passage.

Circle the key word that tells us what water does in the cracks of the rock.

Color what water does when it freezes.

Underline what happens after the frozen water expands in the cracks.

Mountains are always eroding. This is mainly due to the effects of ice, rain, and wind.

At the tops of mountains, water freezes in cracks in the rock. The water expands when it freezes. It causes the rock to split and pieces to break off. This makes mountains jagged.

1 For jagged mountains to form, a number of things must happen. Number the events below to show the **order** in which they happen.

- [ ] The rock splits.

- [ ] The rainwater in the cracks freezes.

- [ ] Rain falls.

- [ ] Jagged mountains are formed.

- [ ] At the tops of mountains, cracks form in the rock.

- [ ] Pieces of rock break off.

- [ ] Rainwater trickles into the cracks in the rock.

Mountains

Read the passage.

Circle **when** the black bear hibernates.

Underline what the bear does before it goes into its den.

Highlight how long the bear spends sleeping.

Color the season that comes after summer.

Underline the season that comes before spring.

Put a box around when the bear comes out of its den.

Some animals survive the winter on a mountain by hibernating. This means they sleep through the coldest months, living on food they have stored.

Black bears in the mountains of North America hibernate every winter.

The bear eats as much as possible in summer and fall. In winter, when there is not much food left, the bear goes into a den to sleep. The den might be a cave, burrow, or the space under some logs on the ground.

The bear's breathing rate drops. It can be as slow as one breath every 45 seconds. It sleeps from four to seven months.

The bear comes out of the den in the spring.

1 What does the black bear do **before** the winter sets in?

_____

_____

2 What does the black bear do **once** the winter sets in?

_____

_____

3 How long does the black bear stay in its den?

_____

4 Which season comes **after** winter?

_____

RI.3.3 Describe the relationship between a series of historical events, scientific ideas or concepts, or steps in technical procedures in a text, using language that pertains to time, sequence, and cause/effect.

183

Prefixes: un, dis, mis

Adding the prefix **un**, **dis**, or **mis** to a word turns it into its opposite; e.g., **un**true, **dis**advantage, **mis**behave.

List ① **Write the word.**

unable _____

disagree _____

mislead _____

unfair _____

dislike _____

unload _____

unlock _____

uncover _____

uneven _____

unhappy _____

unpleasant _____

disappear _____

misbehave _____

unknown _____

mistreat _____

unhealthy _____

mismatch _____

unusual _____

unwrap _____

unlucky _____

② **Sort the words.**

un	dis	mis
___	___	___
___	___	___
___	___	___
___	___	___
___	___	___
___	___	___
___	___	___
___	___	___
___	___	___
___	___	___
___	___	___
___	___	___

③ **Chunks.** Rearrange the syllables to make a list word.

a be/mis/have _____

b pleas/ant/un _____

c u/un/al/us _____

d gree/dis/a _____

e for/un/nate/tu _____

④ **Meaning.** Which list word means?

a To guide in the wrong direction _____

b Not normal _____

c To vanish _____

d To treat badly _____

e To have a different opinion _____

L.3.2.F Use spelling patterns and generalizations in writing words.

Prefixes: un, dis, mis

1 **Revise your spelling list from page 184.** Complete the missing word.

a She was un_____ to visit her friend because she had a cold.

b The incorrect sign will mis_____ them and they will end up in the wrong place.

c The secret agent was trying to un_____ the enemy's master plan.

d We got excited when the rain clouds began to dis_____ .

e I like to mis_____ my socks and wear one blue and one green one.

f We held our noses because of the un_____ smell.

g I usually dis_____ with my brother, but this time he was absolutely right.

h The adventurous explorers traveled into the un_____ part of the woods.

Challenge words

2 **Write the word.**

disbelief _____

dishonest _____

disapprove _____

unnecessary _____

unfamiliar _____

misunderstanding _____

unexpected _____

misplace _____

disconnect _____

uncertain _____

3 **Hidden words.** Find the challenge word.

a uydnunfamiliarueyn _____

b auendishonestaiyn _____

c asyguncertaineuabj _____

d asdsdisapprovejsaih _____

e asermisplaceihyke _____

f asdunexpectedseioy _____

g rtrodisconnectklps _____

h rvmisunderstandingd _____

i mnounnecessarylsto _____

j opdisbelieffste _____

4 **Complete the sentence.**

a She shook her head in _____.

b Their argument started with a simple _____.

c When there is a storm, we always _____ the computer.

d His visit was completely _____.

L.3.2.F Use spelling patterns and generalizations in writing words.

185

Conjunctions

A conjunction joins sentences, clauses or words within a clause. Many **conjunctions** show **cause** (why) or **time** (when, how long); e.g., I put the bag down **because** it was heavy. I saw her **when** I was at the shops.

1 **Complete each sentence with a conjunction from the list.**

| so | when | while | because | until |

a I found the old teddy bear _____ I was tidying the attic.

b You will have to wait _____ your father gets home.

c She peeled the potatoes _____ I chopped the carrots.

d I will take you to the house _____ you can see it for yourself.

e I put an extra blanket on his bed _____ it was cold that night.

2 **Does the underlined conjunction tell WHY or WHEN?**

a We got to the station <u>as</u> the train was leaving. _____

b They will continue playing <u>until</u> someone scores a goal. _____

c We arrived at the stadium <u>before</u> all the other athletes. _____

d I have chosen this book <u>because</u> I like adventure stories. _____

e He kept annoying them <u>while</u> they were doing their work. _____

3 **Replace the underlined conjunction with the correct one from the box.**

| when | because | while | so | until |

a We can't go outside <u>so</u> it is raining. _____

b The house burnt down <u>after</u> we were away. _____

c We waited outside <u>because</u> our coach arrived. _____

d We went to the library <u>until</u> we could exchange our books. _____

e I nearly jumped out of my skin <u>while</u> I saw the hairy spider. _____

L.3.1.H Use coordinating and subordinating conjunctions.

Visual Arts

Making inferences
To make inferences while reading, use clues in the text. The clues help you find the answers that are hiding in the text.

Read the passage.

Underline the sentences that tell us about the liquids used in oil and acrylic paints.

Color the words that show how long it takes oil and acrylic paints to dry.

Oil paint is pigment mixed with oil. It takes a long time to dry. Acrylic paint is pigment mixed with a synthetic liquid. It looks like oil paint but dries faster.

Watercolor paints are pigment mixed with water. They are used on dry or wet paper.

Some artists mix paint with things such as sand, cement, or even straw. This gives the painting an interesting texture.

Highlight the sentence that tells us how watercolor paints are used.

Put a box around the different things artists use to give their painting an interesting texture.

Circle the correct answer for each question.

1 Which is the best **inference**? Oil paint and acrylic paint ...

   a are exactly alike.
   b are made with different liquids.
   c both dry quickly.
   d both take a long time to dry.

2 Which is the best **inference**? Liquid is mixed with pigment to ...

   a bring out the paint's color.
   b make the paint dry faster.
   c give the paint texture.
   d make the paint thinner.

3 From reading the passage, we can **infer** that some artists use paint in creative ways. What is the **clue?**

   a They use paint on dry and wet paper.
   b They mix pigment with different liquids.
   c They mix paint with things like sand, cement, and straw.
   d They mix oil and acrylic paints.

RI.3.1 Ask and answer questions to demonstrate understanding of a text, referring explicitly to the text as the basis for the answers.

187

Visual Arts

Read the
full text

Visual Arts

Read the passage.

Underline the sentence that tells us what a curator does.

Circle the verb that is similar in meaning to *advise*.

Color the sentence that tells us how curators share their knowledge of art.

Highlight the sentence in the last paragraph that sums up one of the curator's most important jobs.

A curator cares for a collection of artworks. Every art gallery has a curator.

Curators make sure that artworks are stored and shown properly. They often suggest which artworks the art gallery should buy.

Curators spend a lot of time studying art. They write about art in books.

Curators plan exhibitions. They decide which artworks to put in an exhibition. Some artworks may need to be borrowed from other places. The curator asks to borrow the artworks and organizes to have them brought to the gallery.

1 We can **infer** that curators know a lot about art. What are the **clues**?

_____

_____

_____

2 We can **infer** that the curator plays an important part in the running of an art gallery. What evidence is there in the text to support this statement?

_____

_____

_____

_____

_____

_____

_____

RI.3.1 Ask and answer questions to demonstrate understanding of a text, referring explicitly to the text as the basis for the answers.

Tricky words

> Some words are trickier to spell than others. Sometimes we add letters that are not supposed to be there. Sometimes we leave out letters. Sometimes we write letters in the wrong order.

List ① Write the word.

before _____

where _____

every _____

once _____

does _____

didn't _____

friends _____

let's _____

its _____

it's _____

quiet _____

clothes _____

minute _____

forward _____

group _____

difficult _____

people _____

often _____

another _____

together _____

② Write the list words in alphabetical order.

_____ _____

_____ _____

_____ _____

_____ _____

_____ _____

_____ _____

_____ _____

_____ _____

_____ _____

_____ _____

③ Fill in the missing letters.

a ___ h ___ r ___

b o ___ t ___ n

c d ___ f ___ ic ___ lt

d ___ oe ___

e e ___ e ___ y

f ___ e ___ 's

g ___ e ___ ore

h i ___ s

i ___ og ___ t ___ er

j it' ___

k o ___ c ___

l c ___ ot ___ e ___

m d ___ dn' ___

n f ___ ___ w ___ rd

o ___ ri ___ nd ___

p ___ n ___ th ___ r

④ Meaning. Which list word means?

a Toward a place or time that is further on _____

b At an earlier time _____

c Hard to do or understand _____

d A number of people or things _____

e Making no sound or noise _____

f Sixty seconds _____

L.3.2.E Use conventional spelling for high-frequency and other studied words and for adding suffixes to base words.

189

Tricky words

1 **Revise your spelling list from page 189.** Underline the mistake.
Write the word correctly.

a I find it dificult to make hard decisions. _____

b Our dog is not very friendly toward other poeple. _____

c We offten go to the park to kick our football. _____

d I was so full I couldn't eat anuther bite. _____

e Hailey and Jimmy work really well togetha. _____

Challenge words

2 **Write the word.**

because _____

really _____

poetry _____

beautiful _____

different _____

interesting _____

February _____

island _____

opposite _____

surprise _____

3 **Word clues.** Which challenge word means?

a pretty _____

b second month _____

c surrounded by water _____

d to catch off guard _____

e for that reason _____

f as different as possible

_____

g something you read or recite

_____

h not the same _____

i fascinating _____

4 **Another way to say it.** Which challenge word could replace the underlined words?

a They were running late <u>as</u> traffic was bad. _____

b My birthday is in <u>the second month of the year</u>. _____

c I found the colors of the sky <u>intriguing</u>. _____

d It was a <u>shock</u> to see my grandparents at my house. _____

e The boys have <u>contrasting</u> opinions about the book. _____

f My mom was <u>very</u> angry about the broken window. _____

L.3.2.E Use conventional spelling for high-frequency and other studied words and for adding suffixes to base words.

Compound sentences

A compound sentence contains **two main clauses**, each of which can stand on its own. The clauses are often joined with a conjunction; e.g., Dogs can bark, **but** they can't talk.

1 **Complete each compound sentence with a conjunction from the list.**

> so   but   and   or   yet

a Farmers grow crops _____ pilots fly planes.

b I have lost my ticket, _____ I can't go to the show.

c She followed the recipe, _____ the cake was a flop.

d He can fix the car himself, _____ he can call a mechanic.

e I put an extra blanket on my bed, _____ I was still cold.

2 **Underline the conjunction in each sentence.**

a Penguins have wings, but they can't fly.

b The faucet was leaking, so we called the plumber.

c She doesn't like broccoli, yet she ate some today.

d You can play tennis, or you can relax in your cabins.

e Logan is a good actor and his sister is a good dancer.

3 **Shade the parts that go together in the same color.**

a	I don't like spinach,	and	you can vote for Janine.
b	He likes ice cream	yet	I am taking him to the vet.
c	You can vote for Brad,	so	I have to eat it.
d	He is very fit,	but	he couldn't finish the race.
e	My dog is sick,	or	she likes candy.

Tales of Invention

Point of view

In nonfiction texts, a writer's point of view can be seen in their word choices. Phrases like "I believe" or "we think" tell the reader the information is the writer's opinion.

Read the passage.

Put a box around Ted Wren's opinion of Alexander Graham Bell.

Color the phrase that gives an opinion of Eliza Bell.

Highlight the words that tell us what most people believe about Alexander Graham Bell's inventions.

Voiceover: Ted Wren continues his series about famous inventors. This week, he looks at Alexander Graham Bell.

I believe Alexander Graham Bell was one of the greatest inventors of the 19th and 20th centuries. He was born in Scotland in 1847. His father, Alexander Melville Bell, was an expert on speech and how the voice works. His mother, Eliza, had poor hearing but many say she played the piano very well.

Alexander Graham Bell moved to the United States in 1871. Five years later he developed the first successful telephone. During his life he took out patents for many inventions, but most people believe that the telephone was his most important invention.

Circle the correct answer for each question.

1 What is the author's **opinion** of Alexander Graham Bell? Alexander Graham Bell was ...

   a an expert on speech.

   b an excellent pianist.

   c a great inventor.

   d a kind man.

2 Which is an **opinion** about Eliza Bell? Many people think Eliza Bell ...

   a played the piano very well.

   b had poor hearing.

   c was Alexander Graham Bell's mother.

   d invented the telephone.

3 How do most people feel about the invention of the telephone? Most people believe it was Alexander Graham Bell's most ...

   a dangerous invention.

   b useless invention.

   c curious invention.

   d important invention.

RI.3.1 Ask and answer questions to demonstrate understanding of a text, referring explicitly to the text as the basis for the answers.

Tales of Invention

Read the passage.

Underline a sentence that shows that Alexander Graham Bell wanted to help people.

In paragraph 1, (circle) the key word that shows that Alexander Graham Bell had a good imagination.

In 1865, Bell studied how the mouth was used to make sounds and speech. In 1870, the Bells moved to Canada, then America. The next year, young Alexander began to teach at a school for deaf people. He experimented with many inventions. Bell came up with the ideas and his assistant, Thomas Watson, made the equipment. They invented an electric speaking telegraph, which we now call a telephone.

On March 10, 1876, Alexander Graham Bell made the first ever telephone. His diary from that day records, "I then shouted into the mouthpiece the following sentence: 'Mr. Watson, come here—I want to see you.' To my delight he came and declared that he had heard and understood what I said."

Highlight the phrase that shows that the telephone was only one of Alexander Graham Bell's inventions.

Color the phrase that tells us how Alexander Graham Bell felt when he discovered that his invention worked.

1 In your **view**, which of the following words could be used to describe Alexander Graham Bell? You may choose more than one word.

a curious b lazy c imaginative d talented

2 Now explain why you chose those words. Use evidence from the text to support your reasons.

_____

_____

_____

_____

_____

_____

Suffix: ness

> Adding the suffix **ness** to an adjective turns it into a noun e.g., soft → soft**ness**.
>
> If the adjective ends in **y**, change it to **i** before adding **ness**; e.g., juicy → juic**i**ness.

List **①** **Write the word.**

darkness _____

goodness _____

kindness _____

stillness _____

sickness _____

brightness _____

sweetness _____

softness _____

slowness _____

greatness _____

happiness _____

emptiness _____

forgiveness _____

readiness _____

wickedness _____

foolishness _____

carelessness _____

eagerness _____

nastiness _____

sharpness _____

② **Word building.** Add the suffix to the base words.

a foolish _____

b careless _____

c eager _____

d bright _____

e sharp _____

f slow _____

g good _____

h dark _____

③ **Chunks.** Rearrange the letters to make a list word.

a ft ne ss so _____

b ti ne ss nas _____

c nd ne ss ki _____

d ill ss ne st _____

e ss ee sw t ne _____

f eat ss ne gr _____

g pi hap ss ne _____

h ss ne giv for e _____

i ss di rea ne _____

j ck ed ne ss wi _____

④ **Name.**

a _____ b _____ c _____ d _____

L.3.2.E Use conventional spelling for high-frequency and other studied words and for adding suffixes to base words.

Suffix: ness

1 **Underline the spelling mistake.** Write the word correctly.

a I like the swetness of honey. _____

b He is filled with wikednes. _____

c I blinked because of the briteness of the light. _____

d She is laughing with happyness. _____

e The opposite of fullness is emptyness. _____

f Her egerness is a pleasure to watch. _____

g His knives are known for their sharpniss. _____

h His sloeness saw him lose the race. _____

i Kinedniss is a wonderful quality to have. _____

Challenge words

2 **Write the word.**

seriousness _____

usefulness _____

selfishness _____

awkwardness _____

loneliness _____

cleanliness _____

friendliness _____

restlessness _____

forgetfulness _____

consciousness _____

3 **Word clues.** Which challenge word means?

a welcoming _____

b likely to forget _____

c clumsiness _____

d awake and aware _____

e worried only about yourself

_____

f feeling alone _____

g not dirty _____

h humorless _____

i being of use _____

4 **Hidden words.** Find the challenge word.

a asucleanlinessyand _____

b sihfforgetfulnessaosiy _____

c vnjdusefulnessirute _____

d rongrestlessnessobep _____

L.3.2.E Use conventional spelling for high-frequency and other studied words and for adding suffixes to base words.

Complex sentences

A **clause** is a group of words with a subject and a verb. A **main clause** makes sense by itself. A **subordinate clause** depends on the main clause for its meaning. Subordinate clauses often start with a **conjunction**. A **complex sentence** contains a main clause and one or more subordinate clauses; e.g., I went to the party (main clause) **because** she invited me (subordinate clause).

1 **Complete each sentence with a conjunction from the box.** Underline the subordinate clause.

| unless | when | if | while | until |

a I saw a lion _____ I went to the zoo.

b They played outside _____ it got dark.

c They will get a reward _____ they complete all the tasks.

d They won't let you in _____ you have a ticket.

e We sat in the car _____ we waited for the storm to pass.

2 **Draw lines to match the main and subordinate clauses.** Circle the conjunctions.

Main clause	Subordinate clause
a We ordered dessert	before I brush my teeth.
b The little boy is crying	I try not to eat it.
c I eat my breakfast	after we had eaten the main course.
d Although I like candy,	whenever I get hungry.
e I make myself a snack	because he scraped his knee.

3 **Write endings for the following sentences.**

a I like this book because _____

_____

b I will help you if _____

_____

c I quickly ran away when _____

_____

L.3.1.I Produce complex sentences.

Spelling

Use this review to test your knowledge. It has three parts—**Spelling, Grammar,** and **Comprehension**. If you're unsure of an answer, go back and read the rules and generalizations in the blue boxes.

You have learned about:

- squ, sch, sph
- irregular plurals
- prefixes: un, dis, mis
- suffix: y
- suffix: ly
- tricky words
- contractions
- trigraph: ear
- suffix: ness

1 **The spelling mistakes in these sentences have been <u>underlined</u>. Write the correct spelling.** 2 marks

   a There were two <u>mouses</u> in the kitchen eating cheese. _____

   b My favorite sweet treat is <u>creemy</u> chocolate gelato. _____

   c Our cheerleading <u>swquad</u> is competing on Saturday. _____

   d Can you help me with this <u>trickie</u> puzzle? _____

2 **Write the correct contraction.** 2 marks

   a they are   _____

   b it is   _____

   c we will   _____

   d we have   _____

3 **Which word correctly completes this sentence?** 1 mark

   The _____ worked hard to make their company a success.

   a womens   b women   c women's   d woman's

4 **Each sentence has one word that is incorrect. Write the correct spelling.** 2 marks

   a We were thersty after our big hike. _____

   b We visit the dentist yaerly to get our teeth checked. _____

   c It started to rain, but luckly Dad had an umbrella in the backpack. _____

   d My bike made a squaky sound when I squeezed the brake. _____

5 **Which word correctly completes this sentence?** 1 mark

   "5, 4, 3, 2, 1," the _____ in Times Square counted down.

   a people   b peoples   c people's   d peoples'

6 **Which word is opposite in meaning to cover?** 1 mark

   a covered   b discover   c miscover   d uncover

7 **Which word correctly completes the analogy?** 1 mark

   Full is to fullness as empty is to _____.

   a emptying   b emptier   c emptiness   d emptyness

Your score

☐

10

Grammar

You have learned about:

- comparative adjectives
- verbs
- conjunctions
- comparative adverbs
- punctuating sentences
- compound sentences
- possessive nouns
- simple sentences
- complex sentences

1 **Complete the following table.** 3 marks

safe	safer	safest
rich		
	more famous	
		heaviest

2 **Complete each sentence with the correct form of the word in parentheses.** 2 marks

a I have never seen anyone run (fast) _____ than Usain Bolt.

b Of everyone, Zac arrived the (early) _____.

c Some stars shine more (bright) _____ than others.

d The old man answered more (wise) _____ than the young prince.

3 **In the following sentences, fill in the missing apostrophes.** 2 marks

a Both dogs leashes are on the bench.

b The lionesses cubs were rolling about on the grass.

c The peoples cheers rang out from the stadium.

d Some flowers petals are starting to fall off.

4 **Write the verbs in the box under the correct heading.** 3 marks

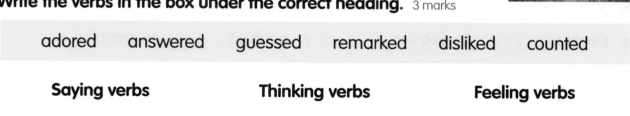

adored   answered   guessed   remarked   disliked   counted

Saying verbs	**Thinking verbs**	**Feeling verbs**
_____	_____	_____
_____	_____	_____

Grammar

5 Write the following sentence with the correct punctuation. 2 marks

how many fours are there in sixteen she asked

_____

6 Complete each sentence with a conjunction from the box. 3 marks

| so | after | while | because | until | but |

a I put on a jacket _____ it was cold.

b I brush my teeth _____ I have breakfast.

c We played outside _____ it got dark.

d I was feeling sick, _____ I went to the doctor.

e Grandpa has milk in his tea, _____ he doesn't take sugar.

f She listens to music _____ she does her chores.

7 Are these simple, compound, or complex sentences? Write the answer next to each sentence. 3 marks

a I rested because I was tired.   _____

b I am very tired today.   _____

c I feel tired, but I'll carry on running.   _____

8 Join the following pairs of sentences with the conjunction in parentheses. 2 marks

a I have a dog. My sister has a cat. (and)

_____

_____

b I hurt my leg. I bumped into the table. (when)

_____

_____

Your score

☐

20

199

The Emu

Read the passage and then use the comprehension skills you have learned to answer the questions.

The emu is Australia's largest bird. It stands about 6 feet tall and has a long, thin neck. Like all birds, it has feathers, two legs, and two wings. Unlike most birds, it cannot fly.

The emu has strong, powerful legs. It can run very fast, reaching speeds of over 30 miles an hour.

Emus eat berries, wild fruits, caterpillars, and grass. They can go for long periods without water, but when they find water, they drink vast amounts. They are good swimmers.

Each year, the female lays between seven and twenty eggs in a nest on the ground. The nest is made of leaves and grass. The eggs are large and greenish-black in color. The male emu sits on the eggs for up to eight weeks until they hatch. The chicks are striped brown and white, so they are well camouflaged in the grass around them. By six months they begin to look like adult birds.

Emus have good eyesight and hearing. This helps them detect predators such as dingoes, eagles, and hawks. When threatened, they defend themselves by kicking out with their strongly clawed feet.

1 How are emus different from most other birds? Emus ... 1 mark   LITERAL

    a have no feathers.   **b** cannot fly.

    c have no wings.   **d** lay eggs in nests.

2 Which sentence is true? Emus ... 1 mark   INFERENTIAL

    a do not need to drink water every day.   **b** cannot run very fast.

    c do not have any enemies.   **d** have poor hearing.

The Emu

3 Give a text clue to support your answer to question 2. 2 marks   CRITICAL

_____

_____

_____

4 Most birds make their nests in trees. Why do emus make their nests on
the ground? 1 mark   CRITICAL

  a The nests are too big for trees.   **b** The eggs are very heavy.
  c There is more food on the ground.   **d** Emus cannot fly.

5 Which emus are eagles and hawks most likely to prey on? 1 mark   INFERENTIAL

  a the females   **b** the males
  c old emus   **d** the chicks

6 Give a text clue to support your answer to question 5. 2 marks   CRITICAL

_____

_____

_____

7 Emus may drink vast amounts of water. This means ... 1 mark   VOCABULARY

  a they drink a little water.   **b** they do not drink often.
  c the water is not clean.   **d** they drink lots of water.

8 How does an emu defend itself? 1 mark   LITERAL

_____

_____

_____

Your score
☐
10

Your Review 4 Scores

Spelling		Grammar		Comprehension		Total
☐	+	☐	+	☐	=	☐
10		**20**		**10**		**40**

Week 1, Day 1
Pg 2

> Later, as Shugg and Katie walked home through the park, Duke stepped out from behind a tree. "Trying to scare me, were you?"
>
> "No," said Shugg.
>
> Duke snatched Shugg's backpack and threw it up into a very tall tree. He stood under the tree with his hands on his hips. "Now let's see you climb up and get it."

1 c **2** d **3** a **4** a **5** a

Week 1, Day 2
Pg 3

> Peter looked down at the backpack poking out from under the bed. Then he shook his head. "Nah! Not even you would bring home an octopus."
>
> Later that night, Shugg raided the pantry. He found a tin of crabmeat and some lobster-flavored noodles. He opened both and pushed them under the bed.

1 Peter
2 under the bed
3 "Nah! Not even you would bring home an octopus."
4 later that night
5 a tin of crabmeat and some lobster-flavored noodles

Week 1, Day 3
Pg 4

1 Check for correct spelling of each word.
2 a mule **b** map **c** sink **d** fled
e log **f** lump **g** black **h** slime
i glad **j** apple
3 Missing vowels are underlined.
a n<u>a</u>me **b** m<u>o</u>le **c** l<u>u</u>mp **d** m<u>i</u>ne
e st<u>o</u>le **f** c<u>u</u>te **g** m<u>u</u>le **h** s<u>u</u>m
4 a map **b** frog **c** egg **d** apple

Week 1, Day 4
Pg 5

1 a name **b** egg **c** mine **d** lid
e frog **f** flame **g** stole **h** mole
i cute
2 Check for correct spelling of each word.
3 a white **b** tiger **c** quake **d** crest
e behave **f** plume **g** spend **h** smash
4 a plume **b** hind **c** extreme **d** spend

Week 1, Day 5
Pg 6

1 Shaded blue: dog, bee, cat, egg, wolf, hen
Shaded red: Africa, Thursday, Miranda, December
2 General people: pilot, singer, explorer
Specific people: Mr. Jones, Cinderella, George Washington
General places: beach, library, museum
Specific places: America, Mount Rushmore, Europe

Week 2, Day 1
Pg 7

> It was Sunday afternoon. I was in my bedroom watching a good movie about aliens when Mom poked her head in. You could tell by the look on her face that she wasn't happy.
>
> "Just look at the state of this room, Jack," she said. "It looks like a pigsty. Turn off the television and clean it up."
>
> "In a minute," I answered, wishing she'd go away. The aliens were about to attack Earth and I wanted to see what was going to happen.

1 c **2** b **3** d **4** a **5** c

Week 2, Day 2
Pg 8

> I asked Mom where she'd put my lunch. Usually it was on the bench.
>
> "Oh, I don't do lunches," Mom said. "You have to make your own sandwiches."
>
> "I'm already late," I grumbled. "You're going to have to drive me to school."
>
> Mom shook her head. "I don't think so, dear. I don't run a taxi service. You'll have to walk."
>
> Grabbing my school bag, I raced out the door. Thanks to Mom, I didn't have a hope of getting to school on time.
>
> On the way I tried to think of a good excuse to tell my teacher. I decided it was easier to tell Mr. Jones the truth.

1 Jack's mom usually made his lunch.
2 Usually it was on the bench.
3 He was going to be late.
4 I didn't have a hope of getting to school on time.
5 He says, "Thanks to Mom …"

Week 2, Day 3
Pg 9

1 Check for correct spelling of each word.
2 a shrub **b** shrine **c** thrust **d** thrush
e throb **f** throng
3 a shr words: shred, shrub, shrug, shrill, shrine, shrink, shrunk, shrimp
b thr words: three, throw, threw, throb, throne, thrill, thrive, thrash, throng, thrust, thrush, thresh
4 Missing consonants are underlined
a <u>thr</u>ow **b** <u>shr</u>imp **c** <u>thr</u>ush **d** <u>thr</u>one

Week 2, Day 4
Pg 10

1 a <u>shrenk</u> shrunk **b** <u>shremp</u> shrimp
c <u>throwne</u> throne **d** <u>throo</u> threw
e <u>thursh</u> thrush **f** <u>shrell</u> shrill
g <u>thri</u> three **h** <u>chred</u> shred
i <u>threll</u> thrill
2 Check for correct spelling of each word.
3 a throat **b** shrapnel **c** through
d throttle **e** enthrone **f** thread
g shrew **h** shrivel **i** shriek
4 a shriek **b** shrivel **c** shrewd **d** thread

Week 2, Day 5
Pg 11

1 a Rover **b** Hunter Street **c** Asia
d Statue of Liberty **e** Globe Theater
f Halloween
2 a Chevrolet **b** Galaxy **c** Queen
d Diego **e** Denali **f** Sea
4 a Eiffel Tower **b** Golden Gate Bridge
c Central Park Zoo

Week 3, Day 1
Pg 12

> A good thing about working in the restaurant is being able to choose any dish I like. Pork buns are my favorite. Some customers are funny and have a joke with you. Old people seem to be easier to talk to.
>
> Others aren't so nice. When they order their food, they say things like, "No salt. No soy sauce. Be quick about it."
>
> I'm very careful when taking down their order, so that I get it right.

1 b **2** d **3** c **4** a **5** c

Week 3, Day 2
Pg 13

> Our school had a Food Day. Mom made me some honey king prawns to take to school. The principal was very impressed with our Hong Kong food.
>
> On Friday, the principal said, "We're going to visit your restaurant, Kalo. My staff and I will be coming tomorrow night for dinner."
>
> My face went red. I wondered what the principal would order. What if he didn't like the food? What if I dropped a spring roll on him? What would my principal say to Mom? I was not the best student in the school.

1 The principal was very impressed with Hong Kong food.
2 *Answers will vary. Suggested answer:* The principal addresses Kalo Li by name and then she uses the pronoun "I" which means it is from her point of view.
3 Kalo is nervous about the principal and his staff not liking the food.
4 My face went red.
5 Kalo thinks she is not the best student in the school.

Week 3, Day 3
Pg 14

1 Check for correct spelling of each word.
2 a market **b** blanket **c** jacket **d** carrot
e rabbit **f** basket **g** trumpet **h** helmet
3 a bandit **b** submit **c** profit **d** target
e market **f** secret
4 Word endings are underlined
a helm<u>et</u> **b** band<u>it</u> **c** carr<u>ot</u> **d** targ<u>et</u>
e rabb<u>it</u> **f** trump<u>et</u> **g** subm<u>it</u> **h** crick<u>et</u>
5 a pocket **b** trumpet **c** helmet

Week 3, Day 4
Pg 15

1 a pocket **b** planet **c** jacket **d** basket
e target **f** market **g** carrot **h** blanket
2 Check for correct spelling of each word.
3 a poet **b** diet **c** maggot **d** quiet
e summit **f** permit
4 a summit **b** deposit **c** cabinet **d** inherit
e permit

Week 3, Day 5
Pg 16

1 a she **b** he **c** them **d** it **e** we
f they **g** I **h** me **i** you **j** us
2 a it **b** it **c** her **d** her **e** she
f her **g** they
3 a we **b** I **c** She **d** he **e** her
f they **g** him **h** them **i** I **j** me

Week 4, Day 1
Pg 17

Annotation answers will vary. Ask children
to talk through responses.

1 b **2** d **3** c **4** a **5** d

Week 4, Day 2
Pg 18

Annotation answers will vary. Ask children
to talk through responses.

1 He felt very annoyed.
2 The tortoise didn't want to leave home
because he was snug and cozy.
3 *Answers will vary. Suggested answer:*
It means to feel comfortable.
4 by making the tortoise carry his home on
his back for the rest of his life
5 *Answers will vary. Suggested answer:*
My brother's big game. I wanted to go
with my family but I felt tired from my
karate tournament. I definitely would have
preferred to stay at home.

Week 4, Day 3
Pg 19

1 Check for correct spelling of each word.
2 a boil **b** toy **c** enjoy **d** spoil
e soil **f** coin **g** avoid **h** voice
i noise **j** royal **k** foyer
3 Missing vowel sounds are <u>underlined</u>
a f<u>oy</u>er **b** l<u>oy</u>al **c** p<u>oi</u>nt **d** j<u>oi</u>nt
e av<u>oi</u>d **f** t<u>oi</u>l **g** ann<u>oy</u> **h** <u>oi</u>l
4 a oil **b** coin **c** toy

Week 4, Day 4
Pg 20

1 a <u>coyn</u> coin **b** <u>joi</u> joy **c** <u>toyle</u> toil
d <u>poynt</u> point **e** <u>joynt</u> joint **f** <u>avoyd</u> avoid
g <u>noyse</u> noise **h** <u>voyce</u> voice
2 Check for correct spelling of each word.
3 a anoint **b** voyage **c** poison **d** employ
e corduroy **f** oyster
4 a choice **b** destroy **c** employ **d** voyage

Week 4, Day 5
Pg 21

1 a huge, big, heavy, gray, wrinkly, large,
enormous, magnificent, smart

2 Smiling: joyful, cheerful, happy, glad, pleased
Grimacing: furious, angry, irritated, annoyed,
mad
Unsure: anxious, scared, worried,
frightened, nervous
3 a funny **b** brown/blue **c** rich/large
d freezing **e** rotten/bad **f** juicy

Week 5, Day 1
Pg 22

> **Narrator:** Somewhere on the seven seas
> is a pirate called Captain Red Beard. The
> Captain has a ship called The Black Beast.
> It is a very fine pirate ship. Captain Red
> Beard and his crew like dropping in on other
> pirate ships and stealing their treasure.
> **Fingers:** Pirate ship on the starboard bow,
> Captain.
> **Captain Red Beard:** Good spotting, Fingers.
> Happy seadogs! Let's meet them.
> Ahoy there fellow pirates! Can my crew
> and I board your ship? We could swap a
> few pirate tales of terror and treasure.

1 b, d **2** a, c, e

Week 5, Day 2
Pg 23

> **Narrator:** Captain Red Beard had an idea.
> **Captain Red Beard:** <u>Nasty</u>? Yes, you are
> the <u>nastiest</u> pirates I have ever met.
> We would like to help you be nasty. You
> must decide on the nastiest thing you
> can do to us. My crew will go below
> decks while you have a nasty little
> meeting about it.
> **Narrator:** Captain Rat thought this was
> a wonderfully nasty idea. His crew all
> argued about what was nastiest. Captain
> Red Beard and his crew went below.

1 He is planning to do something nasty /
steal the pirates' treasure.
2 They are nasty / They steal treasure.
3 *Answers will vary. A suggested answer:*
Captain Rat is going to make Captain Red
Beard and his crew dive in mermaid caves
all day and all night until they find hidden
treasure.
4 *Answers will vary. Suggested answer:*
Captain Red Beard says, "You are the
nastiest pirates I have ever met." I think
diving all day for treasure without a break
would be a very nasty thing to do to
someone else.

Week 5, Day 3
Pg 24

1 Check for correct spelling of each word.
2 a ch words: bench, munch, pinch, ranch,
branch
b tch words: itch, patch, catch, ditch, fetch,
match, pitch, clutch, snatch, stitch, twitch,
sketch, switch, scratch, watch
3 a bench **b** sketch **c** watch **d** branch
e munch **f** ranch
4 a bench **b** watch **c** scratch **d** branch

Week 5, Day 4
Pg 25

1 a <u>ietch</u> itch **b** <u>petch</u> patch
c <u>fech</u> fetch **d** <u>muntch</u> munch
e <u>snach</u> snatch **f** <u>stich</u> stitch
g <u>cach</u> catch **h** <u>dich</u> ditch
i <u>swich</u> switch
2 Check for correct spelling of each word.
3 a hatchet **b** butcher **c** launch **d** satchel
e blotchy **f** scrunch **g** stretch **h** kitchen
4 a quench **b** wretch **c** satchel

Week 5, Day 5
Pg 26

1 a Coach Olson's **b** father's
c man's **d** Professor Redman's
e Captain Westlake's **f** swimmer's
g Aunt Nada's
2 a chef's **b** elephant's **c** whale's
3 a egg's **b** woman's **c** girl's **d** shark's
e boy's **f** rabbit's **g** pirate's

Week 6, Day 1
Pg 27

> Most species of tree are broadleaf
> trees. They often have flat, wide leaves.
> Big, flat leaves can catch lots of
> sunlight, and they need lots of water.
> Some broadleaf trees are deciduous
> and lose their leaves in winter.
> Broadleaf evergreen trees, such as holly
> and orange trees, grow in warmer areas.
> They do not lose their leaves. Broadleaf
> evergreen trees have thicker, waxy
> leaves that often contain oil. The leaves
> can be large, small, long, or short.
> Broadleaf trees are flowering plants.
> New seeds grow from the flowers.

1 d **2** b **3** a **4** c **5** c

Week 6, Day 2
Pg 28

> Many small mammals live in trees.
> Trees provide shelter from wind, rain,
> and other animals. Holes in trees
> become homes for squirrels, and
> acorns are their food. Koalas live and
> feed in eucalyptus trees.
> Many birds live their lives in trees.
> They build their nests in the branches
> or hollows of trees. Trees provide
> fruits, nectar, and seeds for birds
> to eat.
> Millions of insects live in trees. Many
> types of beetles, ants, and butterflies
> depend on trees for food and shelter.

1 acorns
2 eucalyptus trees
3 in the branches or hollows of trees
4 fruits, nectar, and seeds
5 beetles, ants, and butterflies

Week 6, Day 3
Pg 29

1 Check for correct spelling of each word.

2 Missing letters are <u>underlined</u>
a re<u>pair</u> **b** <u>pee</u>r **c** <u>jee</u>r **d** <u>dairy</u>
e s<u>neer</u> **f** <u>fairy</u> **g** <u>sheer</u>/<u>steer</u>
h <u>steer</u>/<u>stair</u>

3 a chair **b** hair **c** pair **d** repair
e cheer **f** dairy **g** veer

4 a hair **b** chair **c** fairy **d** deer

Week 6, Day 4
Pg 30

1 a <u>feir</u> fair **b** <u>deir</u> deer **c** <u>jeir</u> jeer
d <u>leir</u> lair **e** <u>steir</u> steer **f** <u>deiry</u> dairy
g <u>heiry</u> hairy **h** <u>fleir</u> flair **i** <u>steir</u> stair

2 Check for correct spelling of each word.

3 a career **b** pioneer **c** mohair **d** staircase

4 a mountaineer **b** eerie **c** fairly **d** mohair
e pioneer

5 a pioneer **b** mountaineer **c** eerie

Week 6, Day 5
Pg 31

1 a <u>throws</u> **b** <u>catches</u> **c** <u>eats</u> **d** <u>drinks</u>
e <u>drops</u> **f** <u>cleans</u> **g** <u>play</u> **h** <u>read</u>
i <u>drives</u> **j** <u>ride</u>

2 a squawk **b** escapes **c** brushes **d** puts
e crumples **f** pays **g** wags

3 a drizzles **b** weep **c** stroll **d** peers
e sketches **f** munch **g** dozes **h** cleans
i screams **j** protects

4 a go **b** sits **c** dances **d** find

Week 7, Day 1
Pg 32

Stone fruits, fruits with pits, also grow on trees. They have one hard seed covered with soft flesh. Peaches, plums, cherries, and apricots are stone fruits.

Many fruits are quite small. Strawberries, raspberries, and blackberries are all small fruits with lots of seeds. They grow on small plants or bushes in cool areas.

Apples and pears grow on trees in cool areas. They both have a core with small seeds inside. Some apples are grown to make juice to drink.

1 F **2** T **3** T **4** F **5** T **6** F **7** T

Week 7, Day 2
Pg 33

Many animals have a "sweet tooth." Birds and bees drink sweet nectar from flowers, and bears eat honey. People eat sugar made from the dried juice of sugar cane.

Herbs and spices are used in cooking. Herbs such as basil and parsley are used as seasoning. Garlic adds flavor, and chilies are hot and spicy.

Chocolate, vanilla, and cinnamon are also plant flavors. Chocolate is made from seeds. Vanilla is made from seed pods, and cinnamon is ground from the dried bark of a tree.

Many drinks are made using plants. Coffee beans and tea leaves both come from plants. Lemonade is made from the juice of lemons.

1 They are both sweet.

2 Herbs and spices are both used in cooking.

3 Garlic adds flavor, chilli makes the food hot and spicy.

4 Chocolate and vanilla are both plant flavors. Chocolate is made from seeds and vanilla is made from seed pods.

5 Coffee and tea are both drinks. Coffee beans and tea leaves both come from plants.

Week 7, Day 3
Pg 34

1 Check for correct spelling of each word.

2

Singular	Plural
sock	socks
bus	buses
wish	wishes
bird	birds
fox	foxes
mouth	mouths
packet	packets
tomato	tomatoes
piano	pianos
dish	dishes

3 a towers **b** foxes **c** punches
d tomatoes **e** pianos **f** birds
g marches **h** buzzes **i** echoes
j silks **k** packets **l** mouths

4 a tomatoes **b** foxes **c** socks **d** birds

Week 7, Day 4
Pg 35

1 a socks **b** birds **c** tomatoes
d piano **e** bats **f** buses

2 a es **b** es **c** s **d** es **e** s **f** es **g** es **h** es

3 Check for correct spelling of each word.

4 a coaches **b** peaches **c** slippers
d tattoos **e** sopranos **f** superheroes

5 a peaches **b** slippers **c** churches
d superheroes **e** houses

6 a coaches **b** stretchers **c** crosses
d tattoos **e** houses

Week 7, Day 5
Pg 36

1 Tick a, c, e

2 a "Why is Snuffles barking?" asked Simon.
b Georgia said, "Perhaps he wants some attention."
c "Perhaps," said Zoe, "but he might also be hungry."
d "Dad fed him an hour ago," said Annabel.
e "He's been barking a lot lately. Maybe we should give him more attention."

3 a *Answers will vary. Suggested answer:*
The doctor said, "Open wide and stick out your tongue. I need to take a look inside your mouth."
b *Answers will vary. Suggested answer:*
The librarian said, "These answers are all fantastic. I'm glad so many of you enjoyed the book."

Week 8, Day 1
Pg 37

Grasslands are environments in which grass is the main plant, rather than shrubs or trees.

Grasslands need 10 to 40 inches of rain each year. If they get less than this, they turn into deserts. If grasslands get much more rain, lots of trees grow and they become forests.

There are two main types of grassland — savannas (also called tropical grasslands) and temperate grasslands.

1 c **2** d **3** a **4** b **5** c

Week 8, Day 2
Pg 38

The African savanna has cycles of dry and wet seasons.

1 Dry season
Hot winds begin to blow. Grasses die off at the surface, but the roots remain alive. Fires may burn whole areas. Waterholes dry up, causing many animals to migrate. There are often violent thunderstorms before the wet season starts.

2 Wet season
When the rain starts, grass can grow 1 inch in one day

1 hot winds

2 they cause grasses to die off

3 because waterholes dry up

4 animals begin to migrate

5 rain during wet season

Week 8, Day 3
Pg 39

1 Check for correct spelling of each word.

2

Silent *b*	Silent *l*	Silent *h*
lamb	walk	hour
limb	calf	honest
bomb	talk	
numb	palm	
comb	could	
crumb	should	
climb	yolk	
thumb	chalk	
tomb	half	

3 a lamb **b** talk **c** yolk **d** honest
e hour **f** thumb/limb

4 a comb **b** palm **c** thumb **d** lamb

Week 8, Day 4
Pg 40

1 a <u>coud</u> could **b** <u>shoud</u> should **c** <u>tom</u> tomb
d <u>com</u> comb **e** <u>num</u> numb **f** <u>our</u> hour
g <u>lim</u> limb

2 Check for correct spelling of each word.

3 a heir **b** plumber **c** honor **d** exhaust
e shepherd **f** would **g** doubt
h debt **i** folk **j** salmon

4 a salmon **b** plumber **c** debt **d** shepherd

5 a exhaust **b** doubt **c** honor **d** would **e** heir

Week 8, Day 5
Pg 41

1 a of **b** an **c** on **d** several **e** and

2 a a big juicy orange
b several pink and blue balloons
c a big box of delicious candy
d a glass of ice cold fruit juice
e the clown with the funny red nose

3 a cupcake **b** dog **c** cookies **d** soup
e postcard **f** children **g** boat

Week 9, Day 1
Pg 42

On April Fools' Day in 1957, an English TV program showed Swiss farmers picking spaghetti from trees. Hundreds of people called the TV station and asked how to grow spaghetti trees. They were told to "place a **sprig** of spaghetti in a can of tomato sauce and hope for the best." Because spaghetti was an **exotic** food in England at that time, many people didn't know where it came from. They believed that it could grow on trees!

1 b **2** c **3** d **4** c **5** a

Week 9, Day 2
Pg 43

We often believe things we read, especially things that sound scientific. On April 1, 1976 **astronomer** Patrick Moore announced that Pluto would pass behind Jupiter. He said that this would lessen the **gravity** on Earth. If people jumped in the air at the exact moment the planets were in line, they would be able to float — just like astronauts in space. Some people said they had floated up to the ceiling!

1 an astronomer is a scientist who studies planets and space

2 "scientific" tells us an astronomer is knowledgeable about science and the list of the planets, "Jupiter" and "Earth", as well as the dwarf planet "Pluto", suggests science of planets and space

3 "lessen", "air", "jumped", "float"

4 *Answers will vary. Suggested answer:* gravity is less in space so people float but on Earth gravity keeps us on the ground

5 visit space to learn more about our solar system

Week 9, Day 3
Pg 44

1 Check for correct spelling of each word.

2 a selling **b** falling **c** mixing **d** painting
e pouring **f** hoping **g** baking **h** roaring

3 Missing letters are underlined
a roaring **b** lending **c** panting **d** sleeping
e asking **f** carrying **g** trying **h** painting

4

	ing	ed
paint	painting	painted
pour	pouring	poured
roar	roaring	roared
dream	dreaming	dreamed

	ing	ed/d
ask	asking	asked
bake	baking	baked
wipe	wiping	wiped
hope	hoping	hoped

Week 9, Day 4
Pg 45

1 a pannting panting **b** mooving moving
c ruleing ruling **d** lennding lending
e roarring roaring **f** assking asking

2 Check for correct spelling of each word.

3 a scaring **b** blaming **c** snoring **d** crossing
e teasing **f** freezing

4 a praising **b** spraying **c** whining **d** smiling

5 a scaring **b** whining

Week 9, Day 5
Pg 46

1 a is **b** was **c** have **d** am **e** has
f are **g** were **h** had

2 a are **b** has **c** seem **d** is **e** have

3 a is **b** are **c** has **d** have **e** was
f were

REVIEW 1
Spelling
Pg 47

1 a shred **b** secret **c** royal **d** noise

2 c **3** pinch

4 a o **b** a **c** e **d** u

5 a painting **b** climb **c** moving

6 a

Grammar
Pgs 48–49

1 a girl Sam **b** friend Canada
2 a New York **b** Ruby Janey
3 a he her **b** We them
4 a six **b** funny **c** delicious
d orange **e** ancient **f** cold

5 a Olivia's book is on one of those shelves.
b I put two potatoes on my little brother's plate.
c The baby's toys are in the cupboard.
d The city's streets were packed with tourists.

6 a Horses gallop. **b** Dogs bark.
c Rabbits hop. **d** Lions roar.
e Snakes slither. **f** Bees hum.

7 a be **b** please **c** what **d** i'm

8 a forest **b** house **c** kitten **d** cup
9 a are **b** is **c** am **d** was

Comprehension
Pgs 50–51

1 b **2** a

3 *Answers will vary. Suggested answer:* The text says, "The man felt sorry for the tiger", so this tells us he is kind.

4 c

5 *Answers will vary. Suggested answer:* The tiger in the text says, "What a fool you are!", so this tells us he thinks the man is foolish.
6 a **7** d **8** b

Week 10, Day 1
Pg 52

1.	Tree
	Giant, strong
	Climbing, swinging, playing
	Fun among the branches
	Oak

2.	Spaghetti
	Loopy, meaty
	Slurping, slipping, twisting
	Between my fork and mouth
	Yum

3.	Spider
	Hairy, hidden
	Seeing, watching, knowing
	Waits with all patience
	Strikes

Answers will vary. Suggested answer:
Poem 1 Picture of a large oak tree.
Poem 2 Picture of a bowl of spaghetti bolognese.
Poem 3 Picture of a big, hairy spider.

Week 10, Day 2
Pg 53

1.	Zebra
	Black and white stripes
	Grazing on shrubs and leaves
	Sudden snorts, the smell of lion
	Run!

2.	Balloons
	Pink, white and blue
	Bobbing in the garden
	Happy children eating, playing
	Party!

3.	New shoes
	Shiny, squeaky
	Stepping, striding, stomping
	Hurting my heels, pinching my toes
	Ouch!

Answers will vary. Suggested answer:
Poem 1 Picture of zebra running from a lion.
Poem 2 Picture of a children's party.
Poem 3 Picture of a child in new shoes.

Week 10, Day 3
Pg 54

1 Check for correct spelling of each word.

2 a knight **b** delight **c** flight **d** fright
e sight **f** thigh

3 a high **b** night **c** right **d** tight
e light **f** bright

4 a bright **b** sigh **c** fight **d** nigh
e night **f** right

5 Missing letters are underlined
a mighty **b** delight **c** alright **d** slight
e fright **f** night

Week 10, Day 4
Pg 55

1 a <u>hii</u> high   **b** <u>phight</u> fight   **c** <u>ryght</u> right
d <u>alyte</u> alight   **e** <u>myghty</u> mighty   **f** <u>mite</u> might
g <u>nie</u> nigh   **h** <u>shigh</u> sigh
2 Check for correct spelling of each word.
3 a firelight **b** midnight **c** weeknight **d** eyesight
e height **f** frighten **g** righteous **h** plight
i copyright **j** insight
4 a height **b** weeknight **c** eyesight **d** copyright

Week 10, Day 5
Pg 56

1 a thanked **b** pushed **c** spelled **d** blinked
e glowed **f** flapped **g** skipped **h** found
i felt **j** grew **k** thought **l** swam
2 Present tense: speak, dances, stops, reads,
bleed, fries
Past tense: trotted, said, pulled, slipped,
brought, dug
3 a (puts) put   **b** (fall) fell
c (tell) told   **d** (write) wrote
e (teach) taught   **f** (close) closed

Week 11, Day 1
Pg 57

> The Wind and the Sun had a
> competition to see who could make
> the man take off his coat. The Wind
> began to blow as hard as he could.
> He blew directly on the man with a
> whipping, punching wind. The man
> became cold and wrapped his coat
> closely around his body. No matter
> how hard the Wind blew, it was
> useless—the man only held his coat
> more tightly.

1 b **2** a, c, e

Week 11, Day 2
Pg 58

> Now it was the Sun's turn. She
> came out from behind the cloud
> and shone brightly. The man began
> to sweat from the heat and decided
> he could go no further. So he
> stopped, took off his coat,
> and continued his walk.

1 The Sun made the man take off his coat.
2 *Answers will vary. Suggested answer:*
  a The Sun came out from behind the cloud
  and shone brightly.
  b The man began to sweat from the heat
  and decided he could go no further.
  c The man stopped and took off his coat.

Week 11, Day 3
Pg 59

1 Check for correct spelling of each word.
2 a batting **b** tripping **c** grabbing **d** slipping
e fitting **f** winning
3 a winning **b** shutting **c** sitting **d** getting
e running
4 Missing letters are <u>underlined</u>
  a <u>hopp</u>ing **b** <u>runn</u>ing **c** <u>dropp</u>ing
  d <u>chatt</u>ing **e** <u>dripp</u>ing

5 a <u>runing</u> running   **b** <u>driping</u> dripping
c <u>tappping</u> tapping   **d** <u>siting</u> sitting
e <u>sliping</u> slipping   **f** <u>roting</u> rotting

Week 11, Day 4
Pg 60

1 a swimming **b** getting **c** fanning
d rotting **e** clapping **f** winning
g shopping **h** tripping
2 Check for correct spelling of each word.
3 a forbidding **b** submitting **c** squatting
d scrapping **e** wrapping
4 a splitting **b** programming
c regretting **d** permitting

Week 11, Day 5
Pg 61

1 a have **b** are **c** does **d** am
e was **f** has **g** is
2 a are is   **b** has have/had
c are am   **d** do did   **e** have has
f was were   **g** does do
3 a have **b** are **c** are **d** Are
e were **f** was

Week 12, Day 1
Pg 62

> "What's a Whoowuzzler?" asked Olivia.
> "It's an invisible pet," said Sam. "I've
> called mine Wuzzy."
> "And what exactly does Wuzzy look
> like?" asked Olivia, putting her hand
> in the box. It was a shock to find that
> she could feel something small and soft
> even though she couldn't see anything.
> "Well, he kind of looks like a guinea pig
> but he has feathers instead of fur. His
> feathers are (red) with a few (blue) ones
> on his belly," Sam replied.
> Olivia slowly felt the creature in the
> box all over. She had to agree that it
> was exactly what Wuzzy felt like — a
> feather-covered guinea pig.

1 b **2** d **3** c **4** a

Week 12, Day 2
Pg 63

> Back at home, Zazz grew as fast as
> Wuzzy had done, but not from eating.
> The more she bounced the more Zazz
> grew. And she bounced everywhere!
> Wuzzy's (screeching) was no longer the
> problem. Now it was the (thumping) of
> Zazz's long tail.
> The only way to stop the thumping was
> to get Zazz to jump on the bed. When
> Wuzzy saw how much fun jumping on the
> bed was, he wanted to do it too. And,
> when Olivia and Sam saw how much fun
> their invisi-pets were having bouncing on
> the bed, they couldn't help but join in.

1 She bounced everywhere.
2 screeching, thumping
3 *Answers will vary. Suggested answer:*
Zazz is a bouncy invisi-pet with a long tail
that she liked to thump.

4 *Answers will vary. Suggested answer:*
The word 'invisi' suggests Wuzzy and Zazz
might be invisible.
5 They couldn't help but join in by bouncing
on the bed.

Week 12, Day 3
Pg 64

1 Check for correct spelling of each word.
2 ei: reins, vein, veil, beige
ey: prey, whey, they, obey, obeyed, obeying
eigh: eight, weigh, neigh, weighed,
eighth, sleigh, weighing, eighty, eighteen,
eighteenth
3 a eighty **b** whey **c** eighteen **d** neigh
e veil **f** eight **g** obeying
4 a reins **b** prey **c** weigh **d** sleigh
e vein **f** obey

Week 12, Day 4
Pg 65

1 a <u>eyteen</u> eighteen   **b** <u>beighe</u> beige
c <u>weying</u> weighing   **d** <u>eyghth</u> eighth
e <u>obeighed</u> obeyed   **f** <u>eity</u> eighty
2 Check for correct spelling of each word.
3 a survey **b** freighter **c** neighbor **d** feint
e neighing
4 a neighing **b** convey **c** feint
d freight **e** survey **f** lightweight

Week 12, Day 5
Pg 66

1 a give **b** boil **c** ride **d** make
e build **f** watch **g** play
2 a will **b** is **c** am **d** is
e going **f** to
3 a *Answers will vary. Suggested answer:*
Sophia is going to visit her cousins in
Atlanta next week.
  b *Answers will vary. Suggested answer:*
I am going to see The Lion King at the
theater in July.
  c *Answers will vary. Suggested answer:*
The children are going to put on a
performance at the neighborhood fair
next week.

Week 13, Day 1
Pg 67

> Granddad and Lucy wheeled *Crazy Cleaner*
> down to the beach. Lucy set its dials to
> 'underwater' and 'pickup'. She pushed it into
> the water and turned it on. *Crazy Cleaner*
> chugged through the surf.
> "Now we'll find your teeth," said Lucy.
> "Is it supposed to spurt out steam like that?"
> asked Granddad. Steam was pouring from
> *Crazy Cleaner's* engine.
> "Oh no! Something's wrong," said Lucy. "Look!
> It's heading up the beach." *Crazy Cleaner* was
> chugging over the sand towards them.
> "Watch out!" shouted Granddad. They ducked,
> as *Crazy Cleaner* threw a hat at them (and)
> (then) an umbrella.

1 4, 2, 5, 7, 1, 3, 6

Week 13, Day 2
Pg 68

> "Are we there yet? Is this the spot?" asked Granddad, staring into the water.
> Lucy pulled a map out of her pocket and studied it. "Yes, this is it."
> Granddad grabbed his fishing rod. He put a prawn on his hook. Lucy grabbed her fishing rod. Then, she pulled a metal box from her pocket. She tied it to the end of her fishing line.
> "Isn't that *Doggie's Little Helper*?" asked Granddad. "How's that going to find my teeth?"
> "It used to be *Doggie's Little Helper*, but I've fixed it. Now it finds false teeth instead of dog bones," said Lucy.

1 First, Lucy pulled a map out of her pocket and studied it. Meanwhile Granddad put a prawn on his hook.

Then Lucy pulled a metal box out of her pocket. She tied the box to the end of her fishing line. Granddad asked if it was Doggie's Little Helper.

Lucy said she'd fixed it and now it found false teeth.

Week 13, Day 3
Pg 69

1 Check for correct spelling of each word.

2 le: little, table, uncle, apple, candle, bottle, purple, temple, gentle, cattle, bundle, people

el: angel, camel, travel

al: royal, final, normal, local, equal

3 a little   **b** royal   **c** apple
d travel   **e** camel   **f** uncle

4 a table   **b** camel   **c** bottle
d apple

Week 13, Day 4
Pg 70

1 a equal   **b** temple   **c** candle
d camel   **e** table   **f** bottle
g uncle

2 Check for correct spelling of each word.

3 a parcel   **b** example   **c** trouble
d channel   **e** struggle   **f** vehicle
g tribal/floral

4 a floral   **b** vehicle   **c** struggle
d marvel   **e** example

Week 13, Day 5
Pg 71

1 a is coloring   **b** was standing
c were sitting   **d** are planning
e will be cheering

2 a is am/was   **b** were was
c were was/is   **d** close closing
e leave leaving   **f** was were

3

Present progressive	Past progressive	Future progressive
I am crying.	I was crying.	I will be crying.
She is driving.	She was driving.	She will be driving.
They are fighting.	They were fighting.	They will be fighting.
You are selling.	You were selling.	You will be selling.
It is barking.	It was barking.	It will be barking.
She is hiding.	She was hiding.	She will be hiding.
They are shouting.	They were shouting.	They will be shouting.

Week 14, Day 1
Pg 72

> Each member of the forensic team has his or her own job.
> Crime scene investigators (or CSIs) examine the scene of the crime and collect evidence.
> Lab-based forensic scientists carefully analyze this material, often using the latest technology.
> Medical forensic scientists, such as pathologists and dentists are called in if they are needed.

1 c **2** b **3** d **4** a

Week 14, Day 2
Pg 73

> Archeologists are like detectives. They look for clues too. But they're not looking for clues to a crime, they're looking for clues to the past. The archeologists called the iceman "Ötzi", and set out to investigate his mystery.
> Ötzi was wearing his cloak when he died. It was braided from long grasses, and would have been a waterproof layer over his fur clothes. He probably also used it as a blanket or a ground cover.

1 They both look for clues.

2 Detectives look for clues to a crime; archeologists look for clues to the past.

3 as a waterproof layer over clothes, as a blanket or ground cover

4 long grasses and fur

5 natural

Week 14, Day 3
Pg 74

1 Check for correct spelling of each word.

2 a loved   **b** warmed   **c** roasted   **d** kicked
e washed   **f** dusted   **g** smiled

3 Missing letters are underlined
a yelled   **b** cooked   **c** pleased   **d** asked
e poured   **f** roared   **g** mixed   **h** spilled

4 a warmed   **b** washed   **c** kicked   **d** pleased
e spilled   **f** roasted

5

Present tense	Past tense	Present tense	Past tense
smile	smiled	cook	cooked
like	liked	wash	washed
dust	dusted	love	loved
yell	yelled	mix	mixed

Week 14, Day 4
Pg 75

1 a plesed pleased   **b** taimed tamed
c rosted roasted   **d** warmd warmed
e spillid spilled   **f** cooced cooked
g kiked kicked

2 Check for correct spelling of each word.

3 a enjoyed   **b** visited   **c** ordered
d remembered   **e** praised   **f** admired
g appeared   **h** wheeled

4 a appeared   **b** praised   **c** breathed
d ordered   **e** frightened   **f** remembered
g wheeled   **h** admired   **i** enjoyed
j visited

Week 14, Day 5
Pg 76

1 a bread, eggs, milk, and cheese
b cows, goats, sheep, and pigs
c two, four, six, or eight
d shirts, shorts, hats, and shoes
e cars, vans, buses, or trains
f cups, saucers, plates, and bowls

2 toothpaste, toothbrush, comb, and hairbrush

3 a There were forks, spoons, and knives in the picnic basket.

b December, January, and February are the coldest months of the year.

c Yellow, orange, and green are my favorite colors.

d I packed sandwiches, apples, candy, and a bottle of water in my knapsack for the bus ride to Grandma's house.

e I saw lizards, spiders, and snakes at the zoo.

f Did you want to go the movies, the park, or the mall?

g I've been to Beijing, Hong Kong, and Tokyo.

h Dad bought eggs, bread, and milk at the market.

i We have a pet rabbit, two fish, and a very spoilt cat.

j Would you like lasagne, sushi, or burgers for dinner?

k My beach bag contains a towel, sunscreen, and a book to read.

Week 15, Day 1
Pg 77

> It's Darren's birthday, and he's looking forward to his party until ~~he discovers Mother's bunny decorations!~~ He asks Kerry the goldfish for help, but Admiral Bubbles-in-a-Bowl has other ideas.
>
> *Darren Eller Dressed in Yella* helps children see foreign lands—in their own rooms. With a new, (crazy) adventure each week, kids discover that there are (magical) worlds, full of (funny) characters, right in their own homes.

1 c **2** d **3** c **4** b

Week 15, Day 2
Pg 78

> The animation in this show is always bright, on the go, and very detailed. It doesn't have the homemade look that is popular in children's television these days. As children follow Darren's adventures, they explore everyday emotions, such as love, fear, and happiness, and see how Darren and his family respond to challenges. Highly recommended.

1 *Answers will vary. Suggested answer:* The reviewer thinks the animation is good. The reviewer is positive and says, "always bright, on the go, and very detailed." Also the reviewer ends the review positively with "Highly recommended."

2 *Answers will vary. Suggested answer:* The reviewer does believe that children can learn from the program. We know this because the reviewer says that by watching children explore everyday emotions and how the family responds to challenges. We can conclude that by watching how the family responds to challenges, children will be able to respond in their own lives to similar challenges.

3 *Answers will vary. Suggested answer:* I would recommend this program as the reviewer has given it a very positive review. I would make sure it was age-appropriate and would remind children not to have too much screen time each day.

Week 15, Day 3
Pg 79

1 Check for correct spelling of each word.

2 a mane **b** plane **c** groan **d** great
e four **f** knot **g** buy

3 a plain **b** great **c** main **d** four
e scene **f** meat **g** groan **h** by
i seen **j** who's

4 a plane **b** four **c** mane **d** knot

Week 15, Day 4
Pg 80

1 a <u>main</u> mane **b** <u>Who's</u> Whose
c <u>great</u> grate **d** <u>by</u> buy **e** <u>for</u> four
f <u>scene</u> seen **g** <u>meat</u> meet

2 Check for correct spelling of each word.

3 a herd **b** berry **c** rain **d** rein
e heel **f** heal

4 a heard **b** rain **c** bury **d** herd

Week 15, Day 5
Pg 81

1 a flies **b** hats **c** elephants
d loaves **e** berries **f** men **g** notches

2

One	Two	One	Two
ant	ants	potato	potatoes
brush	brushes	half	halves
rabbit	rabbits	wash	washes
knife	knives	tiger	tigers
match	matches	woman	women

3 a girls **b** patches **c** cherries **d** lives
e tomatoes

Week 16, Day 1
Pg 82

1 c **2** b **3** a **4** d **5** b

Week 16, Day 2
Pg 83

1 b, d, g, h, j

Week 16, Day 3
Pg 84

1 Check for correct spelling of each word.

2 silent k: knee, knit, knot, know, knight, knock, knife, knead, knack

silent g: sign, reign, gnat, design, gnome, gnash

silent w: sword, write, wren, wreck, wrong

3 a knot **b** wren **c** sword **d** knight

4 a sword **b** gnome **c** knee **d** gnat
e reign **f** wren

Week 16, Day 4
Pg 85

1 a <u>desin</u> design **b** <u>reck</u> wreck **c** <u>nife</u> knife
d <u>nead</u> knead **e** <u>rite</u> write **f** <u>sin</u> sign
g <u>nit</u> knit

2 Check for correct spelling of each word.

3 a gnarl **b** playwright **c** knuckle
d knapsack **e** wrestle **f** foreign

4 a knuckle **b** knapsack **c** knowledge
d written **e** wreckage

Week 16, Day 5
Pg 86

1 a yours **b** mine **c** their **d** her
e our/its **f** your **g** his

2 a yours **b** his **c** hers **d** theirs
e ours

3 one owner: his, hers, mine, its
more than one owner: our, ours, their, theirs

4 a its **b** yours **c** her **d** ours

Week 17, Day 1
Pg 87

> Forests are full of animals.
>
> There are more (insects) in a forest than any other type of animal. They make up half the mass of all animal life in a rainforest.
>
> About half of all the world's animal species live in tropical rainforests. Hundreds of (bird,) (mammal,) and (reptile) species live in each square mile of tropical rainforest.
>
> Most rainforest mammals and reptiles are arboreal. This means they spend most of their lives in trees.
>
> Small animals, such as (possums) are common in temperate forests.

1 d **2** b **3** e

Week 17, Day 2
Pg 88

> Forest (plants) contain (chemicals) that can be made into (medicines)
>
> Plants make these chemicals to protect themselves from diseases, pests, and plant eaters.
>
> People living in forests make medicines from plants. They use seeds, leaves, fruits, and bark.
>
> Scientists also make medicines from forest plants. The medicines are used to treat asthma, cancer, and many other diseases. The drug Taxol, which is used to treat cancer, comes from the bark of the Pacific yew tree.

1 *Answers will vary. Suggested answer:* Different parts of many plants can be very useful for creating medicines.

2 *Answers will vary. Suggested answer:*
  a The text tells that medicines can be made from plants. The text says, "People in forests make medicines from plants."
  b The text tells us different parts of different plants are used. It lists, "seeds, leaves, fruits, and bark" as all being used for medicines.
  c The text gives the example of a drug that comes from a plant. The drug Taxol treats cancer and it "comes from the bark of the Pacific yew tree."

Week 17, Day 3
Pg 89

1 Check for correct spelling of each word.
2 er: teacher, worker, seller, singer, swimmer, runner, driver, baker, jogger, painter, gardener, climber, printer, wrapper, supporter, builder
or: collector, editor, director, conductor
3 a teacher **b** singer **c** painter **d** baker
  e builder **f** swimmer **g** gardener
4 a collector **b** conductor **c** supporter
  d climber **e** painter

Week 17, Day 4
Pg 90

1 a <u>directer</u> director **b** <u>sellor</u> seller
  c <u>collecter</u> collector **d** <u>runnor</u> runner
  e <u>conducter</u> conductor **f** <u>drivor</u> driver
2 Check for correct spelling of each word.
3 a educator **b** manager **c** navigator
  d decorator **e** knitter **f** foreigner
  g elevator
4 a attacker **b** educator **c** commander
  d elevator **e** exhibitor **f** decorator
  g manager **h** knitter

Week 17, Day 5
Pg 91

1 check: b, c, f
2 a 36 Woodbrook Terrace, Springfield, Massachusetts 01115
  b 95 Alderwood Road, Cleveland, Ohio 44130
  c 794 22nd Avenue, Olympia, Washington 98501
  d 6 Maxwell Place, Denver, Colorado 80222
  e 628 Alabama River Parkway, Montgomery, Alabama 36110
3 84 Beechwood Drive, Savannah, Georgia 31403

Week 18, Day 1
Pg 92

The Australian greater bilby is the largest species of bandicoot. Bilbies are a vulnerable species. Cattle, sheep, and rabbits eat the food they need. Foxes and feral cats prey on them.
To save the greater bilby from extinction, they are bred in captivity and then released back into the wild.

1 a **2** c **3** d **4** c

Week 18, Day 2
Pg 93

Since 1996, many Tasmanian devils have died from a horrible disease. Lumps grow around the devil's mouth that turn into tumors. These spread across the face and body. The tumours make it hard for the devils to eat. Many starve to death.
Scientists are working to save the Tasmanian devil from extinction. They take healthy devils to wildlife parks. These disease-free animals breed with other healthy Tasmanian devils. In the future, they may be released into the wild.

1 tumours that make the devils starve to death
2 The tumours make it hard for them to eat.
3 to make sure the baby Tasmanian devils are healthy
4 that they are able to save Tasmanian devils from extinction

Week 18, Day 3
Pg 94

1 Check for correct spelling of each word.
2 a photo **b** graph **c** whimper **d** phone
  e whale **f** wheat **g** gherkin **h** whisper
3 a phone **b** whale **c** gherkin **d** photo
  e wheel **f** white
4 a phone **b** whale **c** gherkin **d** wheat

Week 18, Day 4
Pg 95

1 wh: why, what, when, white, which, while, whip, whale, where, wheat, whisper, wheel, whimper, whirl
ph: phone, graph, photo, phase
gh: ghost, gherkin
2 Check for correct spelling of each word.
3 a physical **b** whether **c** wheeze
  d ghastly **e** wharf **f** photograph
  g whelp **h** pharaoh **i** ghoul
  j whiskers
4 a pharaoh **b** whiskers **c** wharf

Week 18, Day 5
Pg 96

1 a falls **b** creak **c** splashes **d** ends
  e go **f** live **g** rattles **h** rumbles
2 a picks **b** run **c** rides **d** work
  e sparkle **f** watch **g** hang

REVIEW 2
Spelling
Pg 97

1 a midnight **b** fright **c** regretting
  d weighed
2 camels **3** a
4 a eight **b** survey **c** veil **d** beige
5 a sword **b** gardener **c** editor **d** gherkin
6 a designed **b** cooked

Grammar
Pgs 98–99

1 a ran **b** stalked **c** ate **d** hopped
2 a are **b** am **c** is **d** has
3 a is **b** will **c** are **d** will

4 a The boy will play with his toy soldiers.
  b The children will draw pictures for the art exhibit.
5 a tomatoes, bread, milk, and cheese.
  b elephants, lions, hippos, and giraffes.
6

One	Two	One	Two
baby	babies	monkey	monkeys
child	children	potato	potatoes
wish	wishes	leaf	leaves

7 a his **b** her **c** their **d** your
8 446 Amanda Lane, Montgomery, Alabama 36110
9 a men **b** is **c** has **d** buses

Comprehension
Pgs 100–101

1 d **2** b
3 *Answers will vary. Suggested answer:* The text says that "powerful families ... ruled over ancient China," this tells us that rulers were all from the same family.
4 a **5** b, d **6** b
7 *Answers will vary. Suggested answer:* The text says, "Many died from injury, disease, and starvation", so we know that the work was hard and dangerous.
8 c

Week 19, Day 1
Pg 102

"There's no milk!" said Mom as she slammed the fridge door closed. She turned around and glared at me.
I didn't say a word.
Luckily for me, the kitchen was full of cupcakes, cheese, cookies, bowls of chips, sausage rolls, pickled onions, streamers, hats, and blowers. In the middle of it all was a huge ginger birthday cake with "Happy 80th Birthday" around the edge.
Lucky for me because Mom couldn't see the empty milk carton I'd just been drinking from.

1 d **2** b **3** a **4** c **5** c

Week 19, Day 2
Pg 103

"I'm not going to do it, Mabel," Grandpa was saying. He looked really grumpy and he was shaking his head.
"My teeth are staying in my head until I die." He waggled them with his tongue. They were the most disgusting pair of falsies you've ever seen.
"They're so worn," said Grandma.
"It would be much easier to chew with new ones," said Mom.

1 grumpy
2 He didn't want new false teeth.
3 They were disgusting.
4 because they were worn
5 It would make it easier for him to chew.

Week 19, Day 3
Pg 104

1 Check for correct spelling of each word.
2 ies words: flies, spies, dries, copies, carries, fancies, denies, buries, empties
ied words: tried, cried, fried, tidied, studied, worried, notified, married, hurried, partied, relied
3 **a** tidied   **b** worried   **c** carries   **d** studied
  e hurried   **f** married
4 **a** spies   **b** notified   **c** partied   **d** fried
  e empties   **f** studied

Week 19, Day 4
Pg 105

1 **a** tried   **b** fancies   **c** denies   **d** relied
  e flies   **f** cried
2 Check for correct spelling of each word.
3 **a** qualifies   **b** satisfied   **c** applies
  d occupies   **e** purified   **f** supplies
  g identified   **h** replied   **i** remedied
  j queries
4 **a** remedied   **b** supplies   **c** identified
  d replied   **e** queries   **f** occupies

Week 19, Day 5
Pg 106

1 **a** .   **b** .   **c** ?   **d** ?   **e** !   **f** ?   **g** .
  h .   **i** ?   **j** .
2 **a** What a surprise!   **b** Put it away.
  c What's it about?
3 **a** *Answers will vary. Suggested answer:*
  Where is your dad?
  b *Answers will vary. Suggested answer:*
  Who wrote *Revolting Rhymes*?
  c *Answers will vary. Suggested answer:*
  When are we meeting Grandma and Grandpa?

Week 20, Day 1
Pg 107

> Once upon a time, we used to have lots of frogs living in our pond. We watched their eggs hatch into tadpoles. The frogs croaked a chorus to us every night. They were especially loud when it rained.
>
> We don't have frogs anymore. We have dragons instead. The dragons ate the frogs' eggs, the tadpoles, and the baby frogs. So the big frogs hopped away to find a safer home.
>
> We still have big goldfish living in our pond. The dragons don't eat the adult goldfish, but I think they eat the babies.

1 d   2 c   3 a   4 c   5 b

Week 20, Day 2
Pg 108

> A fat blue-tongued lizard lives under the garage box on our balcony. He comes out when the sun shines and flicks his long, blue tongue trying to catch insects.
>
> Possums hiss in the night and rustle through the trees. They are heading for the banana palms at the back of the house, hoping to find a bunch of ripe bananas for a feast.

1 under the garage box on the balcony
2 when the sun shines
3 He flicks his long, blue tongue.
4 They hiss and rustle through trees.
5 at the back of the house

Week 20, Day 3
Pg 109

1 Check for correct spelling of each word.
2 Missing letters are underlined
  a <u>laugh</u>   **b** <u>d</u>ough   **c** <u>t</u>hought   **d** <u>t</u>aught
3 **a** brought   **b** caught   **c** laughter
  d thought   **e** taught   **f** bought
4 **a** through   **b** dough   **c** bought   **d** cough
  e daughter   **f** rough

Week 20, Day 4
Pg 110

1 **a** <u>plaugh</u> plough   **b** <u>cought</u> caught
  c <u>doughter</u> daughter   **d** <u>noughty</u> naughty
  e <u>caugh</u> cough   **f** <u>thaught</u> thought
  g <u>daugh</u> dough   **h** <u>enaugh</u> enough
  i <u>lough</u> laugh
2 Check for correct spelling of each word.
3 **a** trough   **b** throughout   **c** bough
  d sought   **e** wrought   **f** thorough
4 **a** draught   **b** distraught   **c** onslaught

Week 20, Day 5
Pg 111

1 **a** weakness   **b** warmth   **c** love
  d delight   **e** sadness   **f** beauty
  g length   **h** cruelty   **i** fun
  j pain   **k** hunger   **l** energy
2 **a** softness   **b** hardness   **c** sweetness
  d sourness
3 **a** thought   **b** enjoyment   **c** wickedness
  d anxiety   **e** knowledge
4 **a** strength   **b** health   **c** happiness
  d curiosity   **e** courage   **f** patience
  g imagination   **h** misery   **i** celebration
  j sympathy

Week 21, Day 1
Pg 112

> Ben unpacked the goalie gear from the bag. He pulled on the heavy chest plate, the green-colored leg pads, and the bright orange foot kickers. He put on the safety helmet.
>
> "OK Ben, you're ready for battle," said Coach.
> Battle? That's what it was all right.
> Ben couldn't move. He was afraid to move. He stood like a statue. He wanted to run away. The only trouble was he could barely walk in his leg pads, let alone run.
>
> He'd be the biggest joke in the team. A giant, padded chicken, trying to escape its fate.

1 c   2 d   3 a   4 b

Week 21, Day 2
Pg 113

> The umpire blew the whistle. The game was over.
> "You're a great goalie!" yelled David, patting Ben on the back.
> "Benny, you're on fire," cheered another boy. Ben held his head up high, held his chest out and threw his hands in the air, making high fives with his team.
> Ben had done it. He had gone from yellow-bellied to big brave goalie, and it hadn't hurt a bit.
> Being a goalie wasn't so bad after all. Maybe, just maybe, he'd give it another go next week.

1 He is a great goalie.
2 *Answers will vary.*
3 Being a goalie wasn't so bad after all.

Week 21, Day 3
Pg 114

1 Check for correct spelling of each word.
2 **a** tapped   **b** wrapped   **c** drummed
  d hopped   **e** jutted   **f** snapped
  g slipped   **h** sobbed   **i** dragged
  j slammed
3 **a** tapped   **b** wrapped   **c** slammed
  d slipped   **e** rotted   **f** fanned
4 **a** jutted   **b** petted   **c** batted
  d hummed   **e** grinned   **f** chipped
  g rotted

Week 21, Day 4
Pg 115

1 **a** ripped   **b** hopped   **c** chipped
  d shopped   **e** sobbed   **f** tapped
  g snapped   **h** grinned
2 Check for correct spelling of each word.
3 **a** admitted   **b** equipped   **c** stripped
  d programmed   **e** permitted   **f** embedded
  g acquitted
4 **a** scrapped   **b** acquitted   **c** transmitted
  d shredded

Week 21, Day 5
Pg 116

1 **a** our   **b** their   **c** she   **d** it   **e** them
2 **a** his   **b** she   **c** him   **d** their   **e** we
3 **a** The spectators their   **b** Rosie her
  c The dog its   **d** Bubbles they
  e Simon his

Week 22, Day 1
Pg 117

> When the world was young, Owl did not have feathers. One day, all the world's birds decided to hold a grand ball.
> "How can I go?" sighed Owl. "All the other birds will wear fine suits to the ball. I have no feathers, and they'll make fun of me."
> Hawk heard what Owl had said, and he told the other birds. Every bird gave Hawk a feather, and Hawk passed the feathers to Owl.

> Cinderalla gazed sadly at the dying embers in the fireplace. Her stepsister's cruel words rang through her head.
> "You can't possibly come with us to the grand ball. Everyone will laugh at you in those miserable rags!"
> "But you can go to the ball," said a kind voice. Cinderalla gave a start. "I am your fairy godmother," continued the voice, "and I will give you a fine silk gown to wear."

1 b, e, g, h

Week 22, Day 2
Pg 118

> Owl was so pleased! He flew proudly to the ball.
>
> Owl was having such a wonderful time that he didn't want to give the (feathers) back, so he silently flew away and hid amongst the trees in the forest.
>
> When the party was over, the other birds looked for Owl, but they could not find him. His new feathers helped him blend into the environment.
>
> Now, Owl only comes out to hunt at night, when the other birds are sleeping.

> There are around 200 different owl species. They are nocturnal, which means they are active at night. During the day, they stay hidden in trees.
>
> Most owls hunt insects, small mammals, and other birds. Some species hunt fish. Their powerful talons, or claws, help them catch and kill their prey.
>
> Compared to other birds of prey, owls are very quiet in flight. They are hard to spot during the day. Their (feathers) have a pattern that helps them blend in with the environment.

1 *Answers will vary. Suggested answer:*

a Covering: Owls are covered in feathers.

b Daytime activities: Owls like to hide in trees during the day.

c Nocturnal activities: Owls hunt at night when other birds are sleeping.

d Camouflage: Owls are covered in patterned feathers to help them blend into the environment.

Week 22, Day 3
Pg 119

1 Check for correct spelling of each word.

2 a village **b** orange **c** giraffe **d** cycle **e** danger

3 soft c: city, circus, pencil, grace, rice, cycle, circle, since, dance

soft g: gym, giant, magic, stage, huge, danger, orange, village, engine, giraffe, angel

4 a giraffe **b** circus **c** orange **d** city

Week 22, Day 4
Pg 120

1 a gym **b** engine **c** magic **d** giant **e** stage **f** danger **g** village

2 Check for correct spelling of each word.

3 a intelligence **b** citizen **c** sentence **d** garbage **e** emergency **f** image

4 a garbage **b** lettuce **c** cylinder

5 a garbage **b** sentence **c** emergency **d** lettuce **e** intelligence **f** citizen

Week 22, Day 5
Pg 121

1 a earlier **b** later **c** soon **d** tomorrow **e** immediately **f** sometimes **g** always

2 a later **b** never **c** nightly **d** often **e** last **f** after

3 often

4 a tomorrow **b** before **c** always **d** Sometimes/Usually **e** usually/sometimes **f** never

Week 23, Day 1
Pg 122

> Big things are big trouble. Enormous monsters cause chaos and destruction wherever they go. (Godzilla) is Japan's favourite monster. He first blasted onto Japanese movie screens in 1954 and he's still there today. Godzilla slept on the bottom of the sea until an atomic bomb forced him up to the surface. He looks like a giant *Tyrannosaurus rex* having a temper tantrum. He is angry because he thinks people are destroying the world.

1 d **2** b **3** c **4** a

Week 23, Day 2
Pg 123

The World of Monsters

> Every country has its own stories, or myths, about monsters. Monsters were a good way to explain the unknown. If people didn't know what caused an earthquake, for example, they could say a monster did it.
>
> When Native Americans first dug up dinosaur bones, they thought they were the bones of giant lizards that lived deep in the earth. When these giants shivered, the whole earth quaked!
>
> Many myths tell of monsters with terrible powers. Medusa had (snakes instead of hair.) Anyone who looked at her was turned to stone. But the hero Perseus was able to defeat her by looking at her reflection in a mirror. (Every monster has a weak spot. The trick is to find out where, or what, it is.)

1 as a way to explain the unknown

2 in every country

3 Anyone who looked at her turned to stone.

4 Perseus

5 to find out where, or what its weak spot is

Week 23, Day 3
Pg 124

1 Check for correct spelling of each word.

2 a chose **b** hidden **c** heard **d** shook **e** blew **f** knew **g** meant **h** struck

3 a slept **b** knew **c** struck **d** bled **e** found **f** began **g** chose **h** broke

4 a began **b** mistook **c** found **d** heard **e** blew **f** chose

Week 23, Day 4
Pg 125

1 a awoke **b** heard **c** broke **d** told **e** slept **f** began **g** became

2 Check for correct spelling of each word.

3 a forgave **b** broadcast **c** slung **d** forbade **e** knelt **f** understood

4 a shone **b** built **c** forbade

5 a built **b** broadcast **c** shone **d** forgave **e** spread

Week 23, Day 5
Pg 126

1 a won't **b** don't **c** mustn't **d** it's **e** haven't **f** aren't **g** doesn't **h** I'll **i** I'll **j** should've

2 a haven't **b** could've **c** won't **d** can't **e** might've

3 a let's **b** don't **c** didn't **d** she's **e** we'll

4 Present tense: It isn't here. I can't do it. They aren't happy.

Past tense: We weren't upset. She couldn't go. He wasn't there.

Week 24, Day 1
Pg 127

> Many animals feed on the nectar from flowers. As a result, the animals carry pollen from flower to flower. Many insects feed on (flowers.) Flowers have color and perfume to attract insects. As insects feed on the nectar, they also pick up some pollen. The pollen catches a ride to the next flower. After being pollinated, flowers make seeds.
>
> Birds, bats, and even some lizards are also attracted to flowers.

> Pollination is an important part of the life cycle of plants. Insects such as bees, butterflies, and ladybugs are attracted by the bright colors and smells of certain flowers. They know that these flowers contain the sweet (nectar) that they need to grow and lay eggs. While sucking the nectar, some of the pollen on the flowers sticks to their legs. This pollen gets transferred to the next flower they move to. The pollen fertilizes the flower's egg cells to make seeds.

1 a, b, d, g, h

Week 24, Day 2
Pg 128

> Flowering plants are able to live in many different parts of the world. Rain forests, deserts, and cold mountains are all home to different flowering plants.
>
> Rain forests get plenty of what plants need— rain, warmth, and sunshine— so plants grow in great numbers. A huge variety of flowering plants, such as trees, vines, and other tropical plants, grow in rain forests.

> Rain forests cover about 6% of the earth's surface but contain more than half of the world's plant and animal species.
>
> Rain forests have hot, humid climates. They also have a very high annual rainfall. That's why they are called rain forests!
>
> At least two-thirds of the world's plant species grow in rain forests.

1 *Answers will vary. Suggested answer:*

a Climate: Rain forests have hot and humid conditions with lots of sunshine. They have a very high annual rainfall.

b Plants: More than two-thirds of the world's plant species grow in rain forests including, trees, vines, and other tropical plants.

Week 24, Day 3
Pg 129

1 Check for correct spelling of each word.

2 ary words: diary, salary, burglary, library, summary, glossary   ery words: bakery, cookery, bravery, greenery, misery, grocery, battery, mystery, delivery, nursery, crockery   ory words: factory, victory, memory

3 Missing letters are <u>underlined</u>

a batt<u>ery</u> **b** gloss<u>ary</u> **c** mis<u>ery</u> **d** crock<u>ery</u> **e** green<u>ery</u> **f** summ<u>ary</u> **g** cook<u>ery</u> **h** groc<u>ery</u> **i** burgl<u>ary</u> **j** bak<u>ery</u>

Week 24, Day 4
Pg 130
a diary **b** factory **c** salary **d** victory
e memory **f** mystery **g** library **h** nursery
2 Check for correct spelling of each word.
3 a discovery **b** necessary **c** ordinary
d imaginary **e** dictionary/vocabulary
4 a territory **b** necessary **c** vocabulary
d category **e** ordinary

Week 24, Day 5
Pg 131
1 a when **b** where **c** when **d** where
e how **f** why
2 Across: **1** after **3** at **5** before **6** across
7 in **8** under **9** to

Down: **2** through **4** than **5** beside **8** until

Week 25, Day 1
Pg 132

Desert animals conserve water. They try to avoid very hot and very cold temperatures. The fur or hair of large desert animals keeps them cool. The outer layer of a camel's coat can be 80°F hotter than its body.

Some desert animals, such as the marsupial mole, burrow underground to escape extreme temperatures. It is cooler underground in hot deserts. In cold deserts, it is warmer underground.

1 b **2** c **3** a **4** d

Week 25, Day 2
Pg 133

Deserts often contain oil and iron ore. Drilling for oil and mining can harm desert environments.

Tourists can damage desert water supplies. Vehicles damage desert soils and plants.

When farms are on the edge of a desert, they can damage the fragile desert soil.

Farm animals pound the soil with their hooves. This breaks up the soil. It is then more likely to be eroded by wind and rain.

1 drilling for oil, mining, tourism, farming
2 Tourists can damage desert water supplies.
3 They break up the soil with their hooves, making it more likely to be eroded by wind and rain.

Week 25, Day 3
Pg 134
1 Check for correct spelling of each word.
2 ful: painful, helpful, useful, thankful, hopeful, beautiful, thoughtful, forgetful, truthful, powerful, awful, skilful

less: endless, restless, homeless, careless, harmless, blameless, fearless, tasteless
3 a restless **b** powerful **c** painful **d** awful
4 a restles restless **b** usefull useful
c homeles homeless **d** careles careless
e truthfull truthful **f** fearles fearless

Week 25, Day 4
Pg 135
1 a tasteless **b** painful **c** hopeful **d** endless
e helpful **f** harmless
2 Check for correct spelling of each word.
3 a delightful **b** pointless **c** goalless
d weightless **e** worthless **f** successful
4 a sorrowful **b** respectful **c** successful
d wonderful **e** doubtful
5 a respectful **b** successful **c** delightful
d doubtful

Week 25, Day 5
Pg 136
1 a when **b** where **c** why **d** how
e where **f** how
2 a around the track **b** after midnight
c with both hands
4 a up the hill **b** on a wall
c before midnight **d** over the moon
e with the spoon

Week 26, Day 1
Pg 137

In the 1960s, a few large computers in the USA connected to each other.

If one of the computers broke down, the others would keep working. Universities began to connect computers in the same way. This grew into the Internet—lots of computers connected to each other.

The Internet spread as more people were allowed to use it. Thousands and then millions of computers went online around the world. The speed at which the Internet sent information got much faster.

Today, billions of people use the Internet to find and share information, for entertainment, and to buy and sell goods.

1 *Answers will vary. Suggested answer:*
a Drawing of a few computers connected and people using the internet.
b Drawing of someone watching a television show or buying goods online.

Week 26, Day 2
Pg 138

A storyboard artist turns a film script into a series of drawings to help the people making the story imagine what it is going to look like.
Script for a short film about Humpty Dumpty
Scene 1: Humpty Dumpty is sitting on the castle wall. He waves to the crowd below.
Humpty: Hi everyone.
Humpty stands up. He loses his balance and starts toppling forward.
Humpty: Aaaaaghhhhhhh!
Scene 2: The people in the crowd look down at Humpty's cracked body. Someone takes out a phone and calls an ambulance.
Person in crowd: (*talking on phone*) Come to the castle wall quickly. Prince Humpty's had an accident.
The paramedics patch up Humpty's cracked body.
Paramedic: You're very lucky, Prince Humpty. If the cracks had been any deeper, you would have needed a yolk transfusion.

1 *Answers will vary. Suggested answer:*
a Drawing of Humpty Dumpty toppling off the wall.
b Drawing of paramedics helping put Humpty Dumpty back together.

Week 26, Day 3
Pg 139
1 Check for correct spelling of each word.
2 silent t: listen, fasten, castle, often, rustle, soften, nestle, bristle, thistle, glisten, Christmas, moisten
silent n: solemn
silent u: build, guide, guard, biscuit, guess, guest, guitar
3 a bristle **b** guitar **c** biscuit **d** Christmas
4 Missing letters are underlined
a nestle **b** moisten **c** listen **d** build
e thistle
5 a biscuit **b** guitar **c** castle **d** thistle

Week 26, Day 4
Pg 140
1 a fasen fasten **b** solem solemn
c gitar guitar **d** thisle thistle
e glisen glisten **f** biscit biscuit
g gide guide **h** rusle rustle
2 Check for correct spelling of each word.
3 a guilty **b** column **c** disguise **d** whistle
e hymn **f** hustle
4 a wrestle **b** circuit **c** trestle

Week 26, Day 5
Pg 141
1 a during the night **b** under an umbrella
c with long hair
2 a in the smart suit **b** on the corner
c with happy endings
3 a The Wonderful Wizard of Oz
b The Cat in the Hat
c Alice's Adventures in Wonderland
d The Tale of Peter Rabbit
e The Wind in the Willows
4 The Secret of the Treasure Seekers
5 a in the blue dress **b** with the wand

Week 27, Day 1
Pg 142

Many people work as a team to put on a play. The stage manager has one of the most important jobs.

The stage manager helps the director, actors and stage crew. They plan and run rehearsals, and set up the stage. They listen to the actors to check if they are following the script.

When the play is in performance, the stage manager is in charge. They make sure the stage lights go on and off when they need to. They check that the set changes correctly.

The smooth running of the play is the stage manager's responsibility.

1 c **2** b, c, e

Week 27, Day 2
Pg 143

> William Shakespeare wrote plays more than 300 years ago. One of his most famous plays is Romeo and Juliet.
> The play is set in Italy. It is the story of a young man and woman who fall in love. Their families are enemies who don't want Romeo and Juliet to be together. The story has sword fighting, love, sadness, and humor.
> There have been many interpretations of Romeo and Juliet. An interpretation is the way the play is presented. The story and words remain the same, but the setting changes.
> The Romeo and Juliet story has been used in computer games, songs, operas, ballets, and more than 40 films.

1 *Answers will vary. Suggested answer:*
Shakespeare's famous play, Romeo and Juliet, and its many interpretations over time

2 *Answers will vary. Suggested answer:*
a The text tells us that Romeo and Juliet is a play about a young man and woman who fall in love.
b The text tells us an interpretation is a way of presenting a story and that lots of people have performed Romeo and Juliet for hundreds of years.
c The text tells us that the story has been used in computer games, songs, operas, ballets, and more than 40 films.

Week 27, Day 3
Pg 144

1 Check for correct spelling of each word.
2 Missing letters are <u>underlined</u>
a tea<u>spoon</u>　**b** moon<u>light</u>
c tooth<u>brush</u>　**d** <u>water</u>fall
e <u>base</u>ball　**f** <u>sun</u>rise/<u>sun</u>flower
g <u>rain</u>bow　**h** <u>after</u>noon
i shoe<u>lace</u>　**j** sun<u>flower</u>/sun<u>rise</u>
3 a seafood　**b** footprint　**c** eyesight
d homework　**e** fireworks　**f** butterfly
g airport　**h** keyhole
4 a afternoon　**b** teaspoon　**c** butterfly
d grandson　**e** toothbrush　**f** seafood

Week 27, Day 4
Pg 145

1 a rainbow　**b** moonlight　**c** earring
d sunflower
2 Check for correct spelling of each word.
3 a wheelbarrow　**b** lifeguard
c honeycomb　**d** grasshopper
e supermarket　**f** newspaper
g everyone
4 a thunderstorm　**b** skateboard
c grasshopper

Week 27, Day 5
Pg 146

1 a children's　**b** houses'　**c** tourists'
d acrobats'　**e** monkeys'　**f** mice's
g boys'

2 a butterflies'　**b** shirts'
3 a eggs'　**b** dogs'　**c** women's
d magicians'　**e** crocodiles'

REVIEW 3
Spelling
Pg 147

1 a wrapped　**b** spotted
c rice　**d** oranges
2 a keyhole　**b** toothbrush
c honeycomb　**d** teaspoon
3 a　**4** c
5 a castles　**b** slept　**c** wrote　**d** daughter
6 d

Grammar
Pgs 148–149

1 a ?　**b** !　**c** .　**d** ?
2 a happiness　**b** health
c anger　**d** wisdom
3 a they　**b** she　**c** it　**d** them
4 a he　**b** them
5 a yesterday　**b** soon　**c** weekly
d often
6 a doesn't　**b** won't　**c** we've
d can't　**e** could've　**f** they'll
7 a of　**b** with　**c** to　**d** into
8 a adverb　**b** adjective　**c** adjective　**d** adverb
9 a Ryan said, "I'm getting a bike for my birthday."
b "I sat next to Marcia on the bus," said Maria.

Comprehension
Pgs 150–151

1 c　**2** d　**3** a　**4** b
5 *Answers will vary. Suggested answer:*
The text says that "A sudden gust of wind swooped through the window. It lifted up the plane …" and then it details how the plane made a mess.
6 a　**7** b
8 *Answers will vary. Suggested answer:*
Geraldine was upset to see all of her hard work destroyed.

Week 28, Week 1
Pg 152

> "I've got an illawarry cassary," I said.
> Angus eyeballed me. "A what?"
> "An illawarry cassary. It's a type of meat-eating bird."
> "How come," said Angus, still standing with his elbows across his chest, "we haven't heard about this bird before?"
> "You never asked," I said, and yawned as if I was really bored.
> "We'd like to see it."
> I almost choked in mid-yawn. "You idiot!" I was thinking. Of course they'd want to see it.
> I thought fast. "It always spits on strangers."

1 d　**2** b　**3** a　**4** c

Week 28, Week 2
Pg 153

> Emu gave another howl. In less than a second, I heard three sets of feet running down the driveway.
> I couldn't move. What was going on? Surely they weren't scared of a little wet bantam calling out for his dinner? Hadn't they ever seen a chicken before? I stepped forward to go and get Emu in out of the rain, when I suddenly saw it. From where Angus, Martin, and Alex had stood, Emu was a two-meter-tall, spiky-feathered, war-helmeted, bloodcurdle-screaming, hungry illawarry cassary!
> At school these days we never talk about our pets. And no-one calls me Flake anymore!

1 Three sets of feet ran down the driveway.
2 He thought they were scared of a chicken.
3 They were running away from a hungry illawarry cassary.
4 they never talk about their pets anymore, nobody calls him Flake

Week 28, Day 3
Pg 154

1 Check for correct spelling of each word.
2 Words with squ: squad, squat, squid, squint, square, squish, squeal, squash, squirt, squiggle, squirrel, squeeze, squelch, squeaky, squirm, squall
Words with sch: school, scheme
Words with sph: sphere, sphinx
3 a squeeze　**b** squat　**c** squirrel　**d** square
e school　**f** squeaky　**g** squint　**h** squelch
i squad　**j** squiggle
4 a squid　**b** square　**c** squirrel　**d** sphinx

Week 28, Day 4
Pg 155

1 a squert squirt　**b** skweaky squeaky
c sqweeze squeeze　**d** sqwish squish
e sqweal squeal　**f** sqwash squash
g sqwad squad　**h** sqwint squint
2 Check for correct spelling of each word.
3 a squabble　**b** atmosphere　**c** squawk
d squadron　**e** spherical　**f** squatter
4 a hemisphere　**b** spherical　**c** squadron
5 a squeamish　**b** hemisphere　**c** atmosphere
d squelchy

Week 28, Day 5
Pg 156

1 a funniest　**b** funnier　**c** cutest　**d** cuter
2 Comparing two: more obedient, happier, more pleased, younger, cuddlier, better
Comparing more than two: scariest, weakest, angriest, most anxious, loosest, worst
a coldest　**b** largest　**c** straighter
d most interesting　**e** sweeter

Week 29, Day 1
Pg 157

Hello Will and Vika. You are needed urgently in London, England. Charles E. Worthington needs your help. Something very important is missing. Do not delay. In the corner of the room, under this junk, you will find a parcel containing two transporter wristbands. You must wear these wristbands at all times. They allow you to travel at the blink of an eye and they will keep us in contact.

Remember, this mission is Top Secret. Do not tell anyone you are SWAT agents. You must leave at once.

1 d **2** b **3** d **4** a **5** b

Week 29, Day 2
Pg 158

Once across the park they took a shortcut through some of London's old and narrow cobbled laneways. They came out at Piccadilly Circus.

"This part of the West End is the world's theater capital," said Charlie.

There were signs everywhere saying what was on, what was coming, and who was starring. It was a bustle of restaurants, cafes, theaters, and cinemas. The three of them walked over to a half-price ticket booth. The lady recognized Charlie straight away.

1 It is the world's theater capital.

2 It is a busy place.

3 *Answers will vary. Suggested answer:* People can attend the theater, visit restaurants, cafes, and cinemas.

Week 29, Day 3
Pg 159

1 Check for correct spelling of each word.

2 a cloudy **b** funny **c** floppy **d** stormy
e sleepy

3 Missing letters are underlined.
a creamy **b** greasy **c** watery **d** dusty
e snappy/sleepy/floppy **f** thirsty

4 a funny **b** floppy **c** thirsty **d** snappy

5 a smoky **b** dusty **c** scary **d** windy
e muddy **f** stormy

Week 29, Day 4
Pg 160

1 a windie windy **b** stormi stormy
c mudie muddy **d** scari scary
e smookey smokey **f** creemy creamy
g clowdy cloudy **h** slepi sleepy

2 Check for correct spelling of each word.

3 a spicy **b** sparkly **c** woolly **d** squeaky
e healthy **f** prickly **g** spongy

4 a breezy **b** spongy **c** noisy **d** drowsy

Week 29, Day 5
Pg 161

1 a faster **b** farthest **c** less brightly
d worse **e** harder **f** soonest **g** highest

2 a more politely **b** more neatly
c more frequently **d** less often
e more warmly **f** most clearly
g more healthily

3

Adverb	Comparing two	Comparing more than two
carefully	more carefully	most carefully
proudly	more proudly	most proudly
gracefully	more gracefully	most gracefully
calmly	more calmly	most calmly
recently	more recently	most recently

Week 30, Day 1
Pg 162

Answers will vary, but check which words are circled.

Zed and DD, each wrapped in a pickle jar, tipped over, and began to roll slowly. The bottled hedgehogs picked up speed, bumping and spinning their way down Garbage Hill.

They skipped over old cars and spun off slimy piles of vegetables, getting air as they hurtled forever downwards.

The two jars collided in midair before landing with a PLUNK! DD's jar smashed into a million pieces. Zed's jar spun on the spot until he popped out, fast as a cork. He shot along the sand, grinding his way to a gritty stop.

Answers will vary. Talk through responses to gauge if the child has/hasn't done each answer.

Week 30, Day 2
Pg 163

The three hedgehogs fell into an oasis: a place that only a hedgehog could dream of. Piles of rotting trash filled the air with sweet aromas. It smelt like home.

As the hedgehogs settled on top of the heap, they slowly took in the landscape. Animals of all kinds stared back at them. This was a magical place where all animals were equal and humans did most of the work. "This really is paradise," Ruttel mused.

Answers will vary. Suggested answer: Animals are in different enclosures to help them feel at home. The meerkats are in a small desert enclosure, and penguins have big enclosures with pools for diving and rocks for climbing. Zoo keepers visit the animals throughout the day to feed, play, and observe the different species.

Last year on vacation, we visited the Central Park Zoo. It was fantastic! There were lots of animals to see but I liked the polar bear the best. It was in an enclosure with rocks, a paddling pool, and lots of trees. You could watch the polar bear from different viewing spots and even see underwater.

Week 30, Day 3
Pg 164

1 Check for correct spelling of each word.

2 a can't **b** they'll **c** what's **d** they're
e we've **f** I'll **g** don't **h** I've
i it's **j** won't

3 a I'm **b** they'll **c** don't **d** I'll
e o'clock **f** who's **g** hasn't **h** they're
i we've **j** didn't **k** that's **l** won't
m she's **n** we're

4 a what's **b** isn't **c** can't **d** we're
e I've **f** she's **g** it's **h** we'll
i that's

Week 30, Day 4
Pg 165

1 a Im' I'm **b** Is'nt Isn't **c** did'nt didn't
d should'nt shouldn't **e** Wev'e We've
f oclo'ck o'clock **g** Do'nt Don't
h W'ere We're

2 Check for correct spelling of each word.

3 a couldn't **b** shouldn't
c couldn't **d** shouldn't/doesn't
e would've **f** aren't

4 a must've **b** could've
c shouldn't **d** should've

Week 30, Day 5
Pg 166

1 a "Where did you buy those red shoes?"
b "The neighbors have bought a new car,"
c "Look at that beautiful building!"
d "We are going to the zoo next week."
e "My favorite animals are elephants and giraffes."
f "I asked him a question," "but he didn't answer me."
g "Finish your chores first," "and then you can go and play."

2 a "Are you coming to my party on Saturday?" asked Lily.
b "I got lots of presents for my birthday," said Lucas.
c "Can I watch TV when I've finished my violin practice?" asked Sam.
d Dylan said, "I have lots of aunts, uncles, and cousins."
e "Do all lions have big, bushy manes?" asked the little boy.
f "I've spent hours reading the book," said Myra, "and I still haven't finished it."
g "Would you like a chocolate milkshake?" asked Kai, "or would you rather have a chocolate ice cream?"

3 a "Do you like apple pie?" asked Myrna."
b "I love it," said Laurie," "and I also like choc chip cookies."

Week 31, Day 1
Pg 167

> Fox saw her friend, Bear. Fox had just stolen a string of fish.
>
> "Can you share them with me?" asked Bear.
>
> "No!" snapped Fox. "Catch your own."
>
> "How can I?" asked Bear. "The lake is frozen."
>
> "Cut a hole in the ice," said Fox. "Then, stick your tail in the lake and hold it there as long as you can. It will hurt when the fish grab it. When you think you have enough fish, give your tail a strong tug to pull out the fish."

1 a **2** 3, 1, 4, 2

Week 31, Day 2
Pg 168

> Fox watched as Bear put his tail in the water. Then she ran off laughing. Bear thought he felt some fish bite his tail. But what he was really feeling was water freezing around his tail. When the pain got too great, he pulled at his tail. Nothing happened. He pulled harder. He pulled so hard that his tail broke off. All that was left was a little stumpy tail, like bears have today.

1 after Bear put his tail in the water
2 when he thought he felt a fish bite his tail
3 when the pain got too great
4 It broke off after pulling too hard.

Week 31, Day 3
Pg 169

1 Check for correct spelling of each word.
2 a women **b** scarves **c** mice **d** calves
e men **f** bread **g** lives **h** leaves
i chiefs **j** people
3 Missing letters are <u>underlined</u>
a lo<u>a</u>ves **b** roo<u>f</u>s **c** che<u>f</u>s **d** cli<u>ff</u>s
e ca<u>l</u>ves **f** wo<u>l</u>ves **g** lea<u>v</u>es
4 a geese **b** children **c** mice **d** leaves

Week 31, Day 4
Pg 170

1 a <u>mouses</u> mice **b** <u>sheeps</u> sheep
c <u>gooses</u> geese **d** <u>mans</u> men
e <u>peoples</u> people **f** <u>breads</u> bread
g <u>womans</u> women **h** <u>childs</u> children
2 Check for correct spelling of each word.
3 a thieves **b** spectacles **c** cacti
d furniture **e** shelves **f** beliefs
4 a oases **b** ellipses **c** knives **d** equipment

Week 31, Day 5
Pg 171

1 a asked **b** knows **c** wants **d** yelled
e think **f** enjoyed **g** answered
2 Saying verbs: announced, replied, shouted
Thinking verbs: thought, guessed, remembered
Feeling verbs: wished, loved, hated

3 a shouted **b** believes **c** guessed
d said **e** suppose **f** wonder

Week 32, Day 1
Pg 172

> 1. There was a young lady whose chin,
> Resembled the point of a pin
> So she had it made sharp,
> And purchased a harp,
> And played several tunes with her chin.
>
> 2. There was an old man with a nose,
> Who said, "If you choose to suppose
> That my nose is too long, you are certainly wrong!"
> That remarkable man with a nose.

Answers will vary. Suggested answer:
Poem 1 Picture of a woman playing the harp with her sharp chin.
Poem 2 Picture of a man with a distinctive nose.

Week 32, Day 2
Pg 173

> 1. There was an old man with a beard
> Who said, "It is just as I feared!
> Two owls and a hen,
> Four larks and a wren,
> Have all built their nests in my beard!"
>
> 2. There was a young lady whose bonnet,
> Came untied when the birds sat upon it;
> But she said: "I don't care!
> All the birds in the air
> Are welcome to sit on my bonnet!"

Answers will vary. Suggested answer:
Poem 1 Picture of a man with two owls, a hen, four larks, and a wren nesting in his beard.
Poem 2 Picture of a lady in a bonnet with birds perched on top.

Week 32, Day 3
Pg 174

1 Check for correct spelling of each word.
2 Missing letters are <u>underlined</u>
a <u>strongly</u> **b** <u>surely</u> **c** <u>carefully</u> **d** <u>easily</u>
e <u>luckily</u> **f** <u>angrily</u> **g** <u>slowly</u> **h** <u>busily</u>
i <u>nervously</u> **j** <u>quickly</u> **k** <u>suddenly</u>
3 a angrily **b** easily **c** closely **d** quickly
e happily **f** hopefully
4 a luckily **b** sadly **c** perfectly **d** strongly
e carefully **f** properly

Week 32, Day 4
Pg 175

1 a Hopefully **b** Sadly **c** closely
d Luckily **e** carefully **f** heavily
g happily **h** perfectly
2 Check for correct spelling of each word.
3 a fortunately **b** immediately **c** noisily
d certainly **e** regularly
4 a certainly **b** regularly **c** immediately
d noisily
5 a immediately **b** fortunately
c regularly **d** anxiously

Week 32, Day 5
Pg 176

1 a ? **b** ! **c** . **d** . **e** ? **f** !
2 a I have pens, pencils, highlighters, and an eraser in my pencil case.
b Although I like vanilla ice cream, chocolate ice cream is my favorite.
c She decorated the room with balloons, streamers, and fresh flowers.
d If you're feeling tired, you should rest for a while.
e I've tried calling her, but she doesn't answer her phone.
f I saw puppies, kittens, fish, mice, and rabbits at the pet shop.
g If you must know, I've been to America, Europe, and Asia.
h By the way, those packets, boxes, and tins belong to me.

Week 33, Day 1
Pg 177

> Each leaf of the sundew plant has hundreds of tentacles. Each tentacle has a drop of sticky liquid on the end. When insects come to drink the nectar, they stick to the liquid. As an insect struggles to get free, the sticky tentacles wrap around its body. Now the plant begins to eat the insect's juicy flesh.

1 b **2** b, d, f

Week 33, Day 2
Pg 178

> The giraffes don't eat from one tree for very long. They munch away at a tree for a short time and then they move on.
>
> People watching may think the giraffe is being nice to the tree. The real reason turns out to be very different.
>
> The acacia tree has another way to defend itself — poison
>
> As the giraffe starts to munch on the spiky tree, the tree pushes poison into its leaves. Within 30 minutes the leaves are too poisonous to eat.

1 *Answers will vary. Suggested answer:*
The main idea is that giraffes can only eat from an acacia tree for a short space of time.
2 *Answers will vary. Suggested answer:*
a The text tells us giraffes, "don't eat from one tree for very long."
b The text tells us giraffes don't have a choice about moving trees but that the tree can poison itself.
c The text tells us that the tree produces the poison and "within 30 minutes the leaves are too poisonous to eat."

Week 33, Day 3
Pg 179

1 Check for correct spelling of each word.

2 **a** ear **b** hear **c** year **d** Earth **e** spear

3 **a** fear **b** year **c** wear **d** earn
e hear **f** ear **g** read **h** yearly
i gear **j** learn **k** shear **l** swear
m clear **n** smear **o** pear
p heart/earth **q** spear **r** bear
s near **t** earth/heart

4 **a** heart **b** clear **c** gear **d** smear
e earn **f** pear

Week 33, Day 4
Pg 180

1 **a** spear **b** near **c** bear **d** ear
e Earth **f** learn **g** pear **h** fear

2 Check for correct spelling of each word.

3 **a** weary **b** pearl **c** heard **d** earring
e hearth **f** nearby **g** beard **h** appear
i search **j** dreary

4 **a** beard **b** search **c** nearby **d** dreary

Week 33, Day 5
Pg 181

1 **a** have flown **b** has fed
c have finished **d** are galloping
e has been stalking

2 **a** Woolly mammoths **b** Snakes
c Passengers **d** Restaurants **e** Actors

3 **a** Practice **b** early bird **c** dog
d walls **e** cooks **f** cat
g picture **h** cats **i** broom
j Pride

Day 34, Week 1
Pg 182

Mountains are always eroding. This is mainly due to the effects of ice, rain, and wind.

At the tops of mountains, water freezes in cracks in the rock. The water expands when it freezes. It causes the rock to split and pieces break off. This makes mountains jagged.

1 5, 4, 2, 7, 1, 6, 3

Day 34, Week 2
Pg 183

Some animals survive the winter on a mountain by hibernating. This means they sleep through the coldest months, living on food they have stored.

Black bears in the mountains of North America hibernate every winter

The bear eats as much as possible in summer and fall. In winter, when there is not much food left, the bear goes into a den to sleep. The den might be a cave, burrow, or the space under some logs on the ground.

The bear's breathing rate drops. It can be as slow as one breath every 45 seconds. It sleeps from four to seven months.

The bear comes out of the den in the spring.

1 It eats as much as possible in summer and fall.

2 It goes into a den to sleep.

3 four to seven months

4 spring

Week 34, Day 3
Pg 184

1 Check for correct spelling of each word.

2 un: unable, unfair, unload, unlock, uncover, uneven, unhappy, unpleasant, unknown, unhealthy, unusual, unwrap, unlucky
dis: disagree, dislike, disappear
mis: mislead, misbehave, mistreat, mismatch

3 **a** misbehave **b** unpleasant **c** unusual
d disagree **e** unfortunate

4 **a** mislead **b** unusual **c** disappear
d mistreat **e** disagree

Week 34, Day 4
Pg 185

1 **a** unable **b** mislead **c** uncover
d disappear **e** mismatch **f** unpleasant
g disagree **h** unknown

2 Check for correct spelling of each word.

3 **a** unfamiliar **b** dishonest **c** uncertain
d disapprove **e** misplace **f** unexpected
g disconnect **h** misunderstanding
i unnecessary **j** disbelief

4 **a** disbelief **b** misunderstanding
c disconnect **d** unexpected

Week 34, Day 5
Pg 186

1 **a** when/while **b** until **c** while
d so **e** because

2 **a** when **b** when **c** when **d** why
e when

3 **a** because /while **b** while **c** until
d so **e** when

Week 35, Day 1
Pg 187

Oil paint is pigment mixed with oil. It takes a long time to dry. Acrylic paint is pigment mixed with a synthetic liquid. It looks like oil paint but dries faster.

Watercolor paints are pigment mixed with water. They are used on dry or wet paper.

Some artists mix paint with things such as sand, cement, or even straw. This gives the painting an interesting texture.

1 b 2 a 3 c

Week 35, Day 2
Pg 188

A curator cares for a collection of artworks. Every art gallery has a curator.

Curators make sure that artworks are stored and shown properly. They often suggest which artworks the art gallery should buy.

Curators spend a lot of time studying art. They write about art in books. Curators plan exhibitions. They decide which artworks to put in an exhibition. Some artworks may need to be borrowed from other places. The curator asks to borrow the artworks and organizes to have them brought to the gallery.

1 *Answers will vary. Suggested answer:*
The text tells us that curators are responsible for storing and showing artwork properly. We know to do this, they need to have knowledge of art. We know curators do this in different ways. The text tells us they spend time studying and writing about art.

2 *Answers will vary. Suggested answer:*
The text tells us that curators must "plan exhibitions." To do this, they need to decide what to show, where to borrow the art from, and how they will travel to the gallery. Exhibitions are the main function of art galleries and if curators do this job then they must have an important part to play in art galleries.

Week 35, Day 3
Pg 189

1 Check for correct spelling of each word.

2 another, before, clothes, didn't, difficult, does, every, forward, friends, group, its, it's, let's, minute, often, once, people, quiet, together, where

3 Missing letters are underlined
a where **b** often **c** difficult **d** does
e every **f** let's **g** before **h** its
i together **j** it's **k** once **l** clothes
m didn't **n** forward **o** friends **p** another

4 **a** forward **b** before **c** difficult **d** group
e quiet **f** minute

Week 35, Day 4
Pg 190

1 **a** dificult difficult **b** poeple people
c offten often **d** anuther another
e togetha together

2 Check for correct spelling of each word.

3 **a** beautiful **b** February **c** island
d surprise **e** because **f** opposite
g poetry **h** different **i** interesting

4 **a** because **b** February **c** interesting
d surprise **e** different **f** really

Week 35, Day 5
Pg 191

1 a and **b** so **c** but **d** or **e** yet

2 a but **b** so **c** yet **d** or **e** and

3 a I don't like spinach, but/yet I have to eat it.
  b He likes ice cream and/but she likes chocolate.
  c You can vote for Brad, or you can vote for Janine.
  d He is fit, but/yet he couldn't finish the race.
  e My dog is sick, so I am taking him to the vet.

Week 36, Day 1
Pg 192

Voiceover: Ted Wren continues his series about famous inventors. This week, he looks at Alexander Graham Bell.

I believe Alexander Graham Bell was one of the greatest inventors of the 19th and 20th centuries. He was born in Scotland in 1847. His father, Alexander Melville Bell, was an expert on speech and how the voice works. His mother, Eliza, had poor hearing but many say she played the piano very well.

Alexander Graham Bell moved to the United States in 1871. Five years later he developed the first successful telephone. During his life he took out patents for many inventions, but most people believe that the telephone was his most important invention.

1 c **2** a **3** d

Week 36, Day 2
Pg 193

In 1865, Bell studied how the mouth was used to make sounds and speech. In 1870, the Bells moved to Canada, then America. The next year, young Alexander began to teach at a school for deaf people. He experimented with many inventions. Bell came up with the ideas and his assistant, Thomas Watson, made the equipment. They invented an electric speaking telegraph, which we now call a telephone.

On March 10, 1876, Alexander Graham Bell made the first ever telephone. His diary from that day records, "I then shouted into the mouthpiece the following sentence: 'Mr Watson, come here—I want to see you.' To my delight he came and declared that he had heard and understood what I said."

1 *Answers will vary. Suggested answer:* a, c, d

2 *Answers will vary. Suggested answer:*
Alexander Graham Bell was curious. We know this because of the way he decided to study the mouth to learn about how it made sounds and speech. We can say he was imaginative because of the way the text tells us he "experimented with many inventions." We can also say Bell was talented because in 1876 he ended up making the first ever telephone.

Week 36, Day 3
Pg 194

1 Check for correct spelling of each word.

2 a foolishness **b** carelessness
  c eagerness **d** brightness
  e sharpness **f** slowness
  g goodness **h** darkness

3 a softness **b** nastiness
  c kindness **d** stillness
  e sweetness **f** greatness
  g happiness **h** forgiveness
  i readiness **j** wickedness

4 a emptiness **b** sweetness
  c sickness **d** sharpness

Week 36, Day 4
Pg 195

1 a swetness sweetness
  b wikednes wickedness
  c briteness brightness
  d happyness happiness
  e emptyness emptiness
  f egerness eagerness
  g sharpniss sharpness
  h sloeness slowness
  i Kinedniss Kindness

2 Check for correct spelling of each word.

3 a friendliness **b** forgetfulness
  c awkwardness **d** consciousness
  e selfishness **f** loneliness
  g cleanliness **h** seriousness
  i usefulness

4 a cleanliness **b** forgetfulness
  c usefulness **d** restlessness

Week 36, Day 5
Pg 196

1 a when/I went to the zoo
  b until/it got dark
  c if/they complete all the tasks
  d unless/you have a ticket
  e while/waited for the storm to pass

2 a We ordered dessert after we had eaten the main course.
  b The little boy is crying because he scraped his knee.
  c I eat my breakfast before I brush my teeth.
  d Although I like candy, I try not to eat it.
  e I make myself a snack whenever I get hungry.

3 a *Answers will vary. Suggested answer:*
  I like this book because it recounts the voyagers of explorers from all around the world.
  b *Answers will vary. Suggested answer:*
  I will help you if you promise to help me with my puzzle.
  c *Answers will vary. Suggested answer:*
  I quickly ran away when it started to rain.

REVIEW 4
Spelling
Pg 197

1 a mice **b** creamy **c** squad **d** tricky
2 a they're **b** it's **c** we'll **d** we've
3 b
4 a thirsty **b** yearly **c** luckily **d** squeaky
5 a **6** d **7** c

Grammar
Pgs 198–199

1

safe	safer	safest
rich	richer	richest
famous	more famous	most famous
heavy	heavier	heaviest

2 a faster **b** earliest **c** brightly **d** wisely
3 a dogs' **b** lionesses' **c** people's
  d flowers'/flower's
4 **Saying verbs** answered, remarked
  Thinking verbs guessed, counted
  Feeling verbs adored, disliked
5 "How many fours are there in sixteen?" she asked.
6 a because **b** after **c** until **d** so
  e but **f** while
7 a complex **b** simple **c** compound
8 a I have a dog and my sister has a cat.
  b I hurt my leg when I bumped into the table.

Comprehension
Pgs 200–201

1 b **2** a

3 *Answers will vary. Suggested answer:*
The text says that Emus can "go for long periods without water", and so it can be inferred that they don't need to drink water every day.

4 d

5 d

6 "they are well camouflaged in the grass"

7 d

8 *Answers will vary. Suggested answer:*
Emus defend themselves by kicking their strongly clawed feet.

Reading Eggs *Reading for Third Grade*
ISBN: 978-1-74215-349-0
Copyright Blake eLearning USA 2018

Published by:
Blake eLearning USA
37 West 26th Street,
Suite 201
New York, NY 10010

www.readingeggspress.com

Publisher: Katy Pike
Series writer: Laura Anderson
Series editor: Amy Russo
Editors: Alysha Hodge, Lisa McKay, Megan Smith

Designed and typeset by The Modern Art Production Group
Printed by 1010 Printing International LTD

Week 1 *Shugg's Pet Octopus,* Beverley Boorer, Blake Education, 2003. **Week 2** *No Problem!,* Jan Weeks, Blake Education, 2003. **Week 3** *Kalo Li's New Country,* Hazel Edwards, Blake Education, 1999. **Week 4** *The Lazy Tortoise,* retold by Mark Stafford, Blake Education, 2011. **Week 5** *What Kind of Pirate?,* Lisa Thompson, Blake Education, 2007. **Week 6** *Trees,* Paul McEvoy, Blake Education, 2002. **Week 7** *Plants as Food,* Paul McEvoy, Blake Education, 2002. **Week 8** *Grasslands,* Ian Rohr, Blake Education, 2007. **Week 9** *Hoaxes, Fibs and Fakes,* Lisa Thompson, Blake Education, 2003. **Week 10** *Cinquains,* Mark Stafford (Ed.), Blake Education, 2011. **Week 11** *The North Wind and the Sun,* retold by Mark Stafford, Blake Education, 2011. **Week 12** *Invisi-pets,* Lisa Thompson, Blake Education, 2005. **Week 13** *Toothless!,* Jenny Dobbie, Blake Education, 2003. **Week 14** *It's a Mystery*, Sharon Dalgleish, Blake Education, 2003. **Week 15** *TV Guide,* Mark Stafford, Blake Education, 2011. **Week 16** *Posters*, Mark Stafford, Blake Education, 2011. **Week 17** *Forests,* Ian Rohr, Blake Education, 2007. **Week 18** *Marsupials,* Ian Rohr, Blake Education, 2008. **Week 19** *Chocolate Chuckles,* Pam Harvey, Blake Education, 2000. **Week 20** *Wally the Water Dragon,* Felicity Pulman, Blake Education, 2000. **Week 21** *Yellow-bellied Goalie,* Tracey Hawkins, Blake Education, 2005. **Week 22** *How the Owl Got His Feathers,* retold by Mark Stafford, Blake Education, 2011. **Week 23** *Monsters,* Katy Pike, Blake Education, 2003. **Week 24** *Flowers,* Paul McEvoy, Blake Education, 2002. **Week 25** *Deserts,* Ian Rohr, Blake Education, 2007. **Week 26** *Media,* Mark Stafford, Blake Education, 2007. **Week 27** *Drama,* Mark Stafford, Blake Education, 2007. **Week 28** *The Illawarry Cassary,* Pam Harvey, Blake Education, 2000. **Week 29** *Lookout London,* Lisa Thompson, Blake Education, 2000. **Week 30** *Hedgehogs in the City,* Ned Pike and Freya Pike, Blake Education, 2005. **Week 31** *Why Bear has a Stumpy Tail,* retold by Mark Stafford, Blake Education, 2011. **Week 32** *Limericks,* Mark Stafford (Ed.), Blake Education, 2011. **Week 33** *Plants that Bite Back,* Kate Pike and Paul McEvoy, Blake Education, 2003. **Week 34** *Mountains,* Ian Rohr, Blake Education, 2007. **Week 35** *Visual Arts,* Mark Stafford, Blake Education, 2007. **Week 36** *Tales of Invention*, Mark Stafford, Blake Education, 2011.